CUTS!

CUTS!

Gain Muscle! Lose Fat!

Robert Kennedy

A Perigee Book

Perigee Books
are published by
The Putnam Publishing Group
200 Madison Avenue
New York, NY 10016

Library of Congress Cataloging-in-Publication Data

Kennedy, Robert, date.
  Cuts!/Robert Kennedy.

      p. cm.
  "A Perigee book."
  ISBN 0-399-51477-5 : price
  1. Bodybuilding.   I. Title.
GV546.5.K4455 1989
646.7'5 — dc19   88-9838 CIP

      Printed in the United States of America
        1   2   3   4   5   6   7   8   9   10

Contents

An historic meeting: Tom Platz and Larry Scott.

FOREWORD

When I put a book together I sweat blood! I never write during the day, when interruptions can come at a mile a minute. I can't concentrate sufficiently with people strolling in and out of my office or when the phone rings every few minutes. My books are written at night; frequently past midnight, well into the morning of the next day. There, in the calm and peacefulness of the hour, I can give my best to my work.

This book—*Cuts!*—has been subtitled *Gain Muscle! Lose Fat!* because that is the most important issue in bodybuilding and one that I tell you how to solve within the following pages.

Cuts! is my best book to date. It deals with often-asked questions in a way that makes your success more likely. Many facets of bodybuilding are addressed that have never even been mentioned in other publications.

If you truly want to add more muscle mass to your frame while losing fat, then *Cuts!* is for you. There are no two ways about it. Whether you are a man or a woman, young or not so young, thin or fat, tall or short, black, yellow, white or anything in between . . . following the advice in this book will help you in your quest for physical perfection. Naturally, if you are not al-

Rachel McLish gets set for some incline bench presses.

Ali Mala on the beach at Venice.

ready into a strenuous physical exercise program, then you should consult your family doctor first. Get a checkup. A small percentage of people are not able to tolerate high-voltage exercise such as explained in these pages. This is especially true if you are over forty, or if you are a heavy smoker, or if you have a history of organ or circulatory disorders. It's a good rule to always seek your doctor's advice when starting an exercise program or when beginning a new diet. Chances are, of course, he or she will be delighted that you are doing something positive for your health and well-being, and you will be given the green light to plunge into the bodybuilding lifestyle. But if your doctor does come up with some abnormality, this examination will enable you to get some suitable treatment to correct the problem. Few conditions indeed will demand that you do no exercise at all, but it's a good move to get medical approval nevertheless.

Cuts! gives you everything. Let's get to some of the chapters: I got a kick out of writing the chapter on the eternal question of how to gain muscle while losing fat. This is a subject on everyone's mind. When I give one of my frequent seminars, this point is invariably raised. Now you have an entire book based around the subject.

Many people wonder about nutrition. Well, the new trend is called *grazing,* and whereas animals have been doing it since day one, it is a relatively new eating principle for humans. Truth is, it has been used by bodybuilders for at least three decades, but it's now a fully recognized practice for those who want to gain weight *and* those who need to lose it.

What is the secret in helping both men and women to gain muscle mass? The answer is circulating testosterone. You'll read all about how to keep levels naturally high in a special chapter on the subject.

Ever aware of the popularity of routines, I have set aside a section that gives you special routines to help you maximize progress. If you're like most enthusiastic bodybuilders, you are seeking to get as *built* as you possibly can, and in the shortest space of time.

I just *had* to do the chapter on Vince Gironda's training philosophy because I am forever quoting the man. So much of what he says is true. I am aware that he has a reputation for being a little fanatical, and Vince would be the first to admit it. But, heck! He knows bodybuilding like no one else.

Do you know what *feeder* workouts are? They are the latest bodybuilding rage, responsible for more added muscle on those previously in the throes of a sticking point than any other training system.

If you're going to enter a bodybuilding show, then you had better know how the judges think . . . Chapter 18 gives you the gen on what they are looking for and how you can meet their exact criteria.

Not many bodybuilding books deal with strength training. I've devoted chapter 10 to this. Read it, act on the recommendations, and increase your strength faster than you can spell Hercules!

We all know the importance of the mental side of musclebuilding, but in practice it is often underrated. We become what we can picture clearly in our minds. If we cannot *see* ourselves succeeding, then there is zero chance of a Mr. or Ms. Olympia title. Chapter 3 deals with visualization.

Is that it? No way. I have penned even more chapters on muscle shaping, vascularity, one-set training, increasing pain tolerance, cutting the tempo, aging, workout cycling, protein, and mass building. If I may say so myself, the reading is all good stuff . . . but the results you will get if you follow my suggestions will be little short of . . . miraculous!

Steve Reeves.

1

MUSCLE SHAPING

Yes, You Can!

Stand back from bodybuilding . . . a long way back, and you will see it for what it is. Let's return to your first experiences. When did you first see a picture of a bodybuilder? What did you think at that moment? What about the first time you saw a real bodybuilder in the flesh? Were you shocked, impressed, disgusted?

Many of us were not totally enamoured over bodybuilding when it first entered our lives. Fullest appreciation took a while. We had to grow into it. My first impressions were that bodybuilders looked too symmetrical. They looked plastic, especially when shaved and oiled up. A few looked like plucked chickens ready for the oven! Where was the ruggedness; the natural look? It seemed obvious to me, looking at pictures of the so-called champions, that many were overdeveloped in certain areas. Thighs and pecs frequently appeared too large for the rest of the development. Some individuals seemed totally disproportionate. There were those with arms . . . and little else. One fellow had enormous hanging lats that bulged and creased at the bottom through sheer weight of gravity. He had no legs to speak

of. Yet another guy had huge "riding-britches" thighs and nothing more. There was that seeming multitude of men who possessed enormous pecs . . . fifty-inch chest, no less, but going steady with fourteen-inch calves. . . .

And then there was Steve Reeves. Not as big as some of the others, but he had his own brand of magic. Flawless proportion and shape!

Today bodybuilders use a variety of exercises for each body part. This is commendable. But in itself it is *not* correct. Far better to use just one exercise per body part—the correct exercise to suit your needs—than to indiscriminately choose three or four exercises to build *all aspects* of the muscle. The misguided philosophy behind the multiexercise method is to "hit" all sides of the muscle to develop each to its maximum. This should *not* be your aim. Why not? Let's take the thighs as an example. Some people (dare I say most?) have an aptitude for building very large upper thighs, yet only a small amount of lower thigh. Consequently, those individuals who hit every part hard with high intensity and lots of sets will still end up with huge

The best female abs in the business . . .
Bev Francis.

upper thighs and only mediocre lower thighs. The answer of course is to work the lower and middle thighs with more exercises and more sets than the upper thighs.

Take the abdominals. A ton of exercises work the upper abs, yet very few indeed work the lower abs. Consequently, the upper abs invariably build better than the rest of the waistline. It is pretty obvious to me that most bodybuilders should concentrate on their middle, and especially their lower abs, if they want evenly developed midsections.

The pectorals: Everybody who ever trained knows that the middle and lower pecs develop quickly. But the upper pecs? That's a different story. Especially the upper and outer areas. Most trainers should concentrate 80 percent of their chest training on upper and outer pectoral development. It gives a flared look to the body, increases the visual "V" shape, making your upper shoulder and pectoral area seem wider.

Some people doubt that shape training works. They site Franco Columbu, who has done a million-plus preacher bench curls for his lower biceps, yet to this day possesses "short" biceps. They point to Bill Grant's or Tony Pearson's high calves. There's a flatness to Sergio Oliva's biceps: ditto to a lesser extent to Zane, Dickerson, and Mendenhall. There is doubt that Frenchman Jacques Neuville could build a lower triceps. He needs it to bring his physique up to visual perfection.

Well, does shape training work? Yes and no! A muscle such as the triceps can change shape if you isolate one or two of the three heads when exercising, but you cannot build it lower than where nature has indicated its position on the upper arm. If there are no cells, then none can be enlarged. High calves can never be "brought down." You can maximize the soleus development, but you cannot build lower gastrocnemius than already provided by your individual genetics. Nature has drawn the line.

Because of their separate construction, upper pectorals can be isolated and built separately. The same goes for the thighs, the deltoids, and the back.

The beauty of bodybuilding is that your ap-

Even relaxed, Cory Everson has an amazing physique.

pearance *can change dramatically* when in fact only slight changes have occurred. You have it in your power to bring about these small changes. You can fight disproportion on two fronts. Remember: When muscle is not exercised heavily it shrinks. When muscle is exercised hard it grows. Combine these two principles to shape your body to perfection. *Don't work your overdeveloped areas* and *blitz your under-par sections.* This double-edged battle plan will give you as near to the perfect shape as humanly possible.

SHOULDERS

The shoulders, otherwise known as the deltoid muscle, are three headed. Each head can be more or less isolated with special exercises. Typically, the alternate dumbbell front raise works the front delt section; the lateral (side) raise exercises the outer delt, responsible for important shoulder width, and the bent-over flye exercise trains the rear delt section.

ABDOMINALS

Understand firstly that the pattern of your abdominals cannot be changed. In other words, if your "ridges" are not perfectly in line, and most are not, there is nothing you can do to change things. You have inherited wonky abs. But then so have most of today's champs. People like Mohamed Makkawy, Jacques Neuville, and Scott Wilson have straight abs, but multi–Mr. Universe and Mr. Olympia Chris Dickerson doesn't; neither does Mr. Abdominals himself, "Zabo" Kozewski, and it didn't stop him winning every ab title in the book. Incidentally, straight, evenly balanced abs can be lost by long-term heavy steroid intake. These drugs can widen the linea alba (the central vertical ridge running down the center of your body from the collarbone to the groin) in the midsection region and displace the aesthetic appearance of evenly placed abdominals.

The upper abs always get plenty of stress. Best middle-ab exercises are crunches and roman chair situps going all the way back. Lower abs are worked with leg raises from a bench and hanging leg raises (holding on to a horizontal overhead chin bar).

The obliques can be worked with twists and side bends, but beware of using heavy weights in these exercises. Too much size (thickness) will result, and you could lose your dramatic chest-waist taper.

THIGHS

The upper legs have many aspects that need attention, today more than ever. In the forties and fifties, general thigh mass was enough to win you a contest. Today, judges demand more. You need upper thigh detail (rods). You require bulging hamstrings (thigh biceps). The lower vastus muscles must be developed, as must the inner thighs. . . . Rods are developed by leaning back during thigh extensions and by the performance of lunges. Thigh biceps result from thigh curls (lying builds the lower part; standing builds the peak). Stiff-leg deadlifts also activate the thigh biceps.

The vastus internus and externus (near the knee) are worked best with sissy squats and hack squats. The middle thigh is really hit by the regular back squat, and just below the middle is activated by the front squat (heels on $2\frac{1}{2}$-inch block of wood).

Want more inner thigh (sartorius)? Then use the double pulley squeeze, where while in a sitting position you draw your knees together against pulley resistance.

CALVES

Outer calves are activated more but not isolated if calf raises are performed with the toes pointed inward. Inner calves (diamond shape) are worked when the feet are pointed outward (in the 10 past 2 o'clock position).

CHEST

Lower chest is most activated by the decline bench dumbbell or barbell flyes and presses. Inner chest is worked hardest with narrow grip bench presses (incline or flat) pek dek flyes or cable crossovers. Outer chest is "hit" well with wide-grip parallel bar dips (chin on chest, feet forward of body), flying exercises, and wide-grip bench presses.

Movements like incline barbell and dumbbell flyes and presses stimulate the upper chest development (pectoralis minor). You can also activate this region by lowering the bar to your collarbone instead of to the center of the pectoral region during regular bench presses.

TRICEPS

Like the deltoids, this is a three-headed muscle. The most neglected area is the outer triceps head (situated on the outside of the triceps). Best exercise is the close-grip bench press (elbows out) and the single arm lying supine dumbbell extension. (Lower dumbbell held in right hand to the left pectoral and then straighten. And vice versa.)

Lower triceps (the lower head) is best activated by the bent-over dumbbell extension exercise.

Gary Strydom performs the specialized leg extensions to add cuts in his thighs.

BICEPS

Big controversy here. Truth is, you can lengthen biceps or gain more peak, but only *slightly*. No dramatic changes can be expected. The same goes for the leg biceps.

Best lower biceps exercise is the 35-degree preacher bench curls. Hammer curls (palms facing each other while simultaneously curling dumbbells) slightly lengthen biceps and build upper forearms, improving upper and lower arm tie-in.

Ideal peaking movements include posing (cramping the muscle), concentration curls with light weight, placing emphasis on tensing and flexing during each rep (isotension).

BACK

This is comprised of several parts, all of which should be developed in proportion to one another.

The upper trapezius, running from below the ears to the tops of the shoulders, is built from dumbbell and barbell shrugs. The trapezius in the middle of the upper back is stressed from T-bar rows and seated cable row exercises, especially if the shoulder blades are squeezed together at the conclusion of each repetition.

Lat width is achieved from wide-grip chins and wide-grip pulldowns; two exercises that serve to stretch out the scapulae, a necessary phenomenon if you want really gull-wing lats.

Lower-back development results from the consistent practice of deadlifts or hyperextensions.

A few people find that they have difficulty in developing the lower lat area. The muscle is concave instead of convex during a back lat spread. This is the result of the inability of the scapulae (shoulder blades) to pop out on command. Do plenty of wide-grip chins and try to stretch out the lats at every opportunity. Practice lat spreading every night in the bathroom mirror before going to bed.

In addition, perform the seated cable row with the palms facing upward and pull the handle low into the waist area. Hold in this position for a full second before commencing the next repetition.

THE GLUTES

At one time a true hard-core bodybuilder wouldn't be seen dead performing direct exercises for the buttocks. Somehow it would be considered wrong, too vain perhaps? Glutes were never mentioned; neither criticized nor praised. True, we all knew they were muscles like any other part of our body, yet it was just not appropriate to mention them. How things have changed! Glutes are now in. And the judges look at this area with the same degree of inspection they would any other body part.

Rachel McLish is one of the most conspicuous advocates of direct glute training. She would kneel on a bench with one knee, and with an ankle strap attached to a pulley apparatus. The movement involves raising the leg rearward so that the gluteus muscle is directly involved in the action. Each leg should be alternated with an even number of sets. This exercise can also be performed in the standing position, facing a low pulley apparatus, raising the leg backward while keeping the knee locked.

FOREARMS

The belly of the forearms is best developed by standard wrist curls. The upper forearm is built by reverse curls (keep wrists straight throughout movement) and hammer curls.

You only have to look at a powerlifter's development in comparison to a professional bodybuilder to see that shape building is possible. To my mind only a fraction of the top body-men actually shape train. Most are content to merely use a variety of exercises. The future champions of our sport will come from the ranks of those who plan their training according to their precise requirements. To perfect your proportions so that you sparkle on stage with the magic that comes only with balance, you must shape train.

Marjo Selin: one of the finest female physiques in the world.

Look at the beautiful, weight-trained shape of Detroit's Anita Gandol.

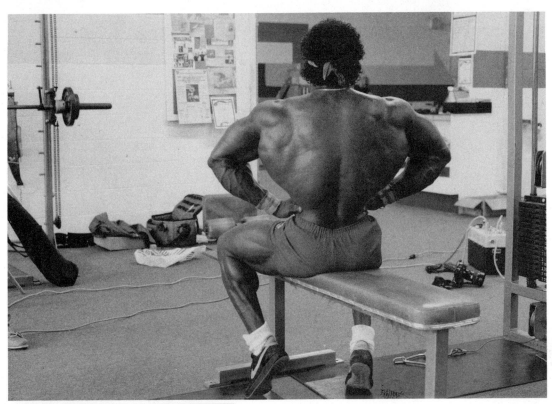

No one does it wider. Tony Pearson.

Thigh squeezes as performed by Aaron Baker.

Gladys Portugues gets oiled by trainer Ken Wheeler.

2

THE GIRONDA FILE

Iron Guru Philosophy

I have made no bones about the fact that I am a great believer in Vince Gironda's musclebuilding philosophy. In fact, Vince and I worked together on a book entitled *Unleashing the Wild Physique* (Sterling Publishing, Inc.). It quickly became a favorite title among those bodybuilders who wanted to build both muscle size and symmetry without resorting to steroids.

Most people who have read Vince's bodybuilding doctrine over the years come down firmly for or against his methods. This is the result of the way he gives advice. He seldom *suggests* a course of action . . . he dictates it. Bang! He is full of dos and don'ts, and seldom allows any leeway for individual interpretation. Vince is black or white. No gray areas exist. He is not wishy-washy. In truth, I wish I were more like him. Why? Because I know that struggling bodybuilders yearn to be told exactly what to do. *How many sets? What number of reps? Precisely what foods, and in what amounts?* Vince fulfills this need. And most times he appears to be right. At least if his record of training top bodybuilders is anything to go by.

Many people dislike the man. Some say he is totally nuts. I love him. He's the last of bodybuilding's real characters. Sure he's nuts. Just as are all hard-core bodybuilders.

Never in my life have I known a man so possessed by bodybuilding. He's an absolute mine of collective information. Ask him anything about building muscle. About diet, competing, posing, cutting up for a contest . . . he'll shoot back an answer before you can say "Vince's Gym." Let's get into some of his crazy philosophy and dissect it for what it's worth.

NO SQUATTING!

Vince is against the general use of back squats, but he will perform them or recommend them to pupils for specific reasons. For example, he often recommends them to some of his women pupils who have naturally flat derrieres. "These people need their butts to be rounded out!" he says. "So I frequently give them a program involving flat-footed squats and leg presses whereby the knees are brought right down to the sides of the ears. It works!"

Many bodybuilders today rely heavily on full squats to build their legs. Its OK for a few who have extremely narrow hips, but most bodybuilders destroy their appearance by performing squats, especially if they eat heavily or take steroids. In both cases the hips spread. The average bodybuilder does not want his or her hips to spread. Squats also cause "turnip thighs" (a Gironda expression). That's the kind of leg development that is characterized by heavy upper-thigh development and nonexistent lower-thigh development. Picture a turnip and you'll get the idea. Again this comes about from heavy back squats, where the individual squats deep, usually with the feet flat on the floor and well apart. Frequently the weight used is so heavy that he rises with the butt first, head between the knees. . . . This of course is a powerlifter's stance, more or less. But bodybuilders are not powerlifters. They

search for aesthetic muscle that is balanced and proportionate. The weight you use is of secondary importance. And if you think only in terms of lifting more and more weight, you will meet a dead end. *Style is the most important part of your training.* It must be adapted to enhance your physique. It must not be thrown out the window to feed a power-hungry ego.

Personally, I think that squats are the best exercise of all. They build size in the upper legs like no other exercise in existence. But they must not be abused, especially in conjunction with someone who is inclined to be "heavy" in the hip area or who has a tendency to be overweight.

NO RUNNING!

Larry Scott, a Gironda pupil, doesn't like running. "We bodybuilders want to build the biggest, most vascular muscles to shock our friends. Running

Bob Tessier and Vince Gironda.

Larry Scott returns to the beach at Venice, at the age of fifty.

doesn't help the production of muscular bulk.'' Vince also concludes that running goes against everything the bodybuilder strives for. He claims it even lowers male hormone production. ''At least that's what the scientific tests conclude,'' he says. True enough, running does seem contrary to a hard-core bodybuilder's aims, but it does have its use when contest competition comes around. Few activities burn fat faster than running, and therefore to a bodybuilder in need of speedy fat reductions, running has its place. It is also an excellent builder of cardiovascular efficiency, which is another term for fitness. True, it's not important in itself, to the bodybuilder, but without it you do not have the right to call yourself *fit!*

Marjo Selin.

NO BENCH PRESSING!

Now here is where Vince gets a little tricky. On one hand he tells us that the bench press is no good for building pecs, yet he does advocate *neck presses,* which are really bench presses, but using a wide grip and taking the bar to the throat instead of the upper chest. ''The best pectoral-building exercise,'' says Vince, ''is the wide-grip parallel bar dip (hands thirty-two to thirty-six inches apart), holding the feet forward of the body, chin on chest.'' Vince concludes that this exercise is a real pec builder because it not only adds mass but builds the all-important upper and outer areas of the pectorals, thus giving the chest a wide, flared appearance.

The bench press is a great pec-building exercise in most cases, but some bodybuilders really don't get much effect from it. I definitely agree with Vince that the wide-grip parallel bar dip exercise is extremely effective.

CUT THE AB EXERCISES

''Too much stomach exercising can put an end to your gains in the mass department,'' says the Iron Guru. He has explained several times that the abdominal muscles can be very sensitive to strenuous training, and too much can shock the nervous system into preventing healthy gains in muscular body weight. This does not apply to all bodybuilders, many of whom train their midsections really hard two or three times a week, but thin or nervous types (ectomorphs) must keep their ab training to a minimum if really fast gains in mass are desired.

Vince is also adamantly against doing standard situps for the midsection. ''It's the most asinine, useless exercise known. Situps are not even an abdominal exercise," he says. The alternative? Crunches and side bends. Did you know that Mr. Gironda actually threw someone out of his gym for performing situps? Only the day before, the individual concerned had asked Vince which were the best abdominal exercises.

Vince spent twenty minutes talking to the guy and demonstrating his line of ab movements. Needless to say, situps were not recommended. But, lo and behold, the next day our would-be champion came out onto the gym floor, and right in full view of the Guru, he performed three sets of regular situps. That was the end of him!

Larry Scott works his abs on the lat machine.

At one of his heaviest body weights, Arnold Schwarzenegger is interviewed in Australia by Mike Walsh.

3

CREATIVE VISUALIZATION

Making It Work for You!

Arnold Schwarzenegger has freely talked about his use of it. Two-time Mr. Olympia Frank Zane used it to aid him in building his classic physique, and the incomparable Steve Reeves was said to have put it to effective use back in the 1950s. There's even evidence that the great Napoleon Bonaparte used it to help conquer his foes and build his amazing empire.

What is it that these great men used to help them reach the pinnacle of success? The answer is *creative visualization.*

In his own words let Arnold tell us how he used creative visualization to help build his incredible physique. "It became part of my routine to start out every day with total concentration. The way I did it was to play out in my mind exactly what I was going to lift, how I was going to pull on my muscles, and how it would feel. I programmed myself to do it. I saw myself doing it. My mind was always in touch with my body."

That kind of talk would probably have generated some pretty loud laughs before bodybuilding became so popular, but over the last few years it has become quite clear that there is a lot more to creative visualization than just a lot of bunk.

Creative visualization works to the extent that some authorities such as Charles Garfield, author of *Peak Performance,* believe that almost anything is possible with effective use of creative visualization. Garfield relates his own experience in this respect when he tells how he used it to add more than forty pounds to his best-ever bench press after *not* training for several years.

What exactly is creative visualization? Very simply, it's a technique in which you use your mind to make positive things happen in your life. For instance, as a youngster Arnold wanted to build the greatest pair of biceps in the world. So, each night before going to sleep, he created a mental picture of his biceps growing. He actually *saw* his arms growing bigger and more massive with each passing day, and soon he began to develop the kind of biceps that he saw in his mind.

Granted, Arnold Schwarzenegger is not your average bodybuilder: he has a highly unusual capacity for developing muscle. But in the same sense he did use his mind and the creative visualization process to compound his mass-building capacity. The result was the development of a physique that many believe is unparalleled even today.

Arnold did it, and you can too. You may not be able to develop a physique as impressive as Arnold's, but creative visualization can help you get more out of bodybuilding and strength training. The possibilities are staggering. You can use it to help gain more strength, muscle size, or greater definition. Even lagging body parts or troublesome injuries can be aided by use of creative visualization. That is not to imply that you won't have to train hard when you're doing creative visualization, for it is not a miracle worker. It cannot replace training or a lack of effort, but it can compound the effects of your training many times over and help you reach goals and heights that you never thought yourself capable of.

So how do you use creative visualization? There are five basic steps to putting it into play.

Step one is to decide exactly what you want to accomplish or what you want to happen. You might want to develop larger shoulders. That's a good goal — just be specific.

Step two. Form a clear-cut mental picture of exactly what you want to happen. Using the example of building your shoulders, lock into a mental image of your shoulders growing bigger and bigger. See and feel your shirts straining to accommodate this newfound muscle size. See yourself as already having accomplished the goal regardless of the stage of your actual development. See those huge shoulders in your possession. Now!

Step three. Bring that mental picture into your imagination as often as you can. Whether you are daydreaming, driving in the car, or just killing some time, call up that mental image. *See*

those shoulders filling up the screen, and feel that massiveness as if it were on your frame at that very moment.

An excellent time to bring up your mental pictures is just before you go to sleep, when you're in a relaxed state and very receptive to the effects of creative visualization. Just as Arnold did, you may want to make it a practice to perform creative visualization every night just before dropping off to sleep.

Step four. Always think and speak about your goal in positive terms. Words can have a powerful effect on you, so control your inner dialogue so that it constantly reinforces what you want to accomplish.

For instance, instead of saying, "I think I'll have a shot at building the shoulders I'm after," say, "My shoulders are growing with each and every day, and I will do whatever it takes to push them to the size I desire." In other words, surround your mental picture with an aura of positive reinforcement.

Step five. Combine your creative visualization with progressive relaxation as often as possible. This is slightly different from Step Three in the sense that here you literally orchestrate relaxation.

This is what you do: Put yourself in a comfortable position, either sitting or lying in a spot where you won't be disturbed. Now let yourself become totally relaxed by alternately contracting and relaxing your muscles.

Begin with your toes. Contract them vigorously upward, holding them in a rigid position for a count of six. Then completely let them go and feel the warmth and deep relaxation that runs through them.

This is the exact type of deep relaxation that you want to induce throughout your body. Do this by alternately contracting and relaxing all of your major muscle groups, including your legs, buttocks, abdomen, chest, shoulders, back, arms, and even your face and scalp. This technique will take about ten minutes to cover your entire body.

Once you are totally relaxed, let the image of what you want to accomplish come into your mind. See those huge shoulders and feel that extra mass. Keep this image in your mind as long as it feels right. Explore it from every angle and really try to experience it. This is also a very good time to bring in your positive self-talk, as this will doubly reinforce the image.

The frequency with which you use this technique is up to you, but I would recommend that you try to use it at least three times per week.

Creative visualization. What you tell yourself and envision can become true—so go for it!

Frank Zane.

Gladys Portugues using a barbell for bent-over rows.

Arnold Schwarzenegger works his rear delts.

*Amazing Gary Strydom
shows his pec muscularity
to N.P.C. president
Jim Manion.*

DAVID

Triceps pressdowns, Tom Platz style.

California's amazing Shawn Ray trains on the thigh-extension apparatus.

4

BUILDING MASS

Adding Muscle to the Frame

Nothing is more frustrating to the skinny man or woman than trying to put on weight. Often it seems that whatever one does, however hard one trains, and however many calories are consumed, the scales show the same figure day after day, month after month. . . .

Boy, it's frustrating. I recall that from the age of seventeen, well into my early twenties, my weight was stuck at 155 pounds and my arms would not budge from 14$\frac{1}{8}$ inches. I would train like crazy and my arms would pump to 14$\frac{3}{4}$, but by the next time I taped them there would be that measurement again. Fourteen and one-eighth inches!

How does one gain weight? First of all, let's agree that when we talk of adding mass, we mean muscle. No one should want to add fat. Years ago the bodybuilding world found itself engulfed by the "bulk craze." Everyone wanted to be bigger. Low-body-fat percentage was not even a consideration. Bodybuilders didn't care about shape, proportion, symmetry, definition, separation, or anything else . . . other than possessing huge size. They wanted to be big men, like today's heavyweight Olympic and powerlifters. How did they do it? In a word, *milk*. Everyone

was drinking it by the gallon. Of course, plenty of other food was also consumed, but milk was the principal nutrient for upping the mass. Training was pretty basic. The so-called authorities of the day would advise a Monday, Wednesday, Friday whole-body routine of squats, presses, rows, deadlifts, curls, and bench presses. Three or four sets of six to eight reps was most often prescribed. And it worked. The bodybuilders gained bulk, not because they were training harder, but because they were eating more, especially milk! And there was one more thing. In order to maximize weight gains, bodybuilders were told to be downright lazy. They were *instructed* to slow down their metabolic rates by never running when they could walk; never walking when they could sit; never sitting when they could lie down. Believe me, never in the history of bodybuilding were there so many divorce petitions brought before the courts for the repeated "offense" of husbands refusing to take out the garbage for fear of losing precious body weight. Bodybuilders would refuse to shop, perform manual work, or even go for a stroll . . . all for fear of losing a quarter of an inch from their arms. Needless to say, all other sports and recreation were frowned upon. Sexual intercourse itself was curtailed in order to pay homage to the god of mass and might! This craze is now over, and we have returned to stressing pure muscle mass and matching proportions — but a few members of the ''bulk-at-all-cost brigade'' still walk the earth. They are called pro wrestlers!

I understand the need for mass. I spent years in very heavy training, eating everything I could get my hands on. To be honest, I wanted to get rid of my skin-and-bones body so badly that I could not have cared one iota if it was *all* fat! I would have given anything to look half as good as Hulk Hogan.

But times have changed. Today bodybuilders want to gain mass as fast as possible, but they are also aware that this mass should be *lean mass* (pure muscle) not *bulk mass* (fat and muscle).

To achieve this we must pay homage to everything that has been learned before. But we must not go to extremes. It is a good idea to hold off on performing too many other activities that will burn up precious calories, but let's be sensible. An occasional swim, a game of table tennis, a brisk walk . . . where's the harm? Not to mention the joys of lovemaking. . . . And, yes, milk is an excellent aid in helping us gain weight, but to drink more than a couple of quarts a day is too much for most people. You are inviting obesity. Take milk in at times when you require musclebuilding sustenance. You will seldom need more than a glass or two at a time. If you are inclined to put on fat, you may find that milk is not the right food for your constitution. You will end up with more flab than muscle!

Training for mass still confuses many bodybuilders. The reason for this is that mass can be gained through different forms of training. My job is to let you know the *best* form of training to gain mass, which I will discuss in this chapter. Many bodybuilders conclude that the best way to attain huge size is to follow the training methods of people who have the most massive bodies.

Cable upright rows as performed by the awesome giant Gary Strydom.

This would be a mistake. In my day the biggest fellow around was Doug Hepburn. He was superseded by a new colossus from Georgia, Paul Anderson. Other giants to follow were Yuri Vlasov, Leiono Zhabotinsky, and Vassily Alexeev, all supersized Russian lifters. Today we have an array of huge professional wrestlers and strongmen such as Hulk Hogan, Paul Orndorff, Ricky Steamboat, Grizzly Brown, and phenomenal Ted Arcidi.

Now, theoretically it would seem reasonable to conclude that since these are the most massively built people on the face of this earth, in order to maximize our own size we should follow their style of training. Most of them use only basic exercises like bench presses, squats, cleans, and deadlifts . . . and their repetitions per set average — wait for it — three!

So does that mean you will grow fastest using only a handful of exercises and performing just three reps per set? No. These people are big *in spite of* their using a limited number of exercises and low repetitions, not because of it. Their training was designed first and foremost to build strength. The fact that they are also huge is a result of their natural aptitude for largeness. Most of the aforementioned, for example, have wrists around nine inches in circumference. Now, how does that compare to *your* wrist measurement?

It is true that your routine should be kept reasonably brief, and that basic multijoint exercises are the best mass-builders, but we have other considerations. . . . We must build a well-proportioned body; one that is symmetrical and balanced. It has to look massive *and* attractive.

If you don't care about looking good and just want to gain bulk, perform squats and bench presses twice a week and spend the rest of the time in bed eating! You'll gain weight . . . big, blubbery, ugly weight. And you're welcome to it.

As for the rest of us, I suggest that you alternate a special mass-building program with a more advanced routine (containing more exercises), so that more than basic muscles are worked as your bodybuilding experience grows.

Sets and reps should be varied. Not only does this practice keep the muscles guessing (preventing them from falling into a rut), but you are attacking all the aspects of size building by performing both high and low repetitions. Muscle cells (fibers) grow best from six to eight repetitions each set, while mitochondria, corpuscles, etc., take on additional size from higher reps, leaning into the twelve, fifteen, twenty, and even higher categories.

Sleep and rest are important to anyone trying to gain muscular body weight, but there is no need to go overboard. Never get fewer than seven hours' sleep each night. If you must party, then make sure it's at a time when you can sleep in the following day to catch up on your missed sleep. Some bodybuilders find that they need more than seven hours, especially on days following heavy workouts. I have known several top bodybuilders who sleep nine or ten hours each night, and they feel better for it.

The question of rest is a difficult one. Canada's Nimrod King, Bertil Fox, Ali Mala, and a host of other champions take an afternoon nap when in serious training. This *muscle-sleep,* as it

Judging the sides: Boyer Coe, Bob Paris, and Sergio Oliva.

has been termed, is a luxury most working men and women cannot afford, so let me hasten to add that scores of top titles have been trained for, and won, by individuals who never took muscle-sleeps during the day.

On the other hand, I would be misleading you if I said that rest is unimportant. Many a road laborer, mineworker, bricklayer, or foundry worker has found out the difficulties of gaining weight while working at a physically demanding job, but again there have been exceptions. Lou Ferrigno made terrific progress while working eight-hour shifts as a sheetmetal worker, and Sergio "The Myth" Oliva won the Mr. Olympia title while holding a regular job working in 120-

degree temperatures in a Chicago steel foundry.

Ideally, bodybuilding enthusiasts should be office workers, teachers, accountants, lawyers, sales clerks, designers, graphic artists, librarians . . . get the picture? Jobs that require little or limited physical exertion are best, since they don't rob us of vital energy for that all-important training session.

A word about nutrition. Athletes, and particularly bodybuilders, fail to understand the importance of eating fruit and vegetables. These foods work hand in hand with lean meats, eggs, fowl, fish, and milk products to build your muscles to their maximum potential. Do not snack on a Mars Bar or a Kit-Kat—eat an apple, a plum, an or-

The amazing Barbarian twins.

ange. Fruit and vegetables are just as important as the protein foods when it comes to proper body functioning and maximum muscular growth. Also, when you make fresh fruit and vegetables a big part of your diet, it is unlikely that you will be burdened with high body-fat levels. There is little chance of gaining much in the way of excess weight, since we are dealing with foods that are wholesome, natural, and not loaded with refined sugar.

Working out for ultimate mass should be precisely planned. Your schedule should be of moderate length—better too short than too long. Work each body part twice weekly. Perform five sets of each exercise. Hit on the correct exercise

style and tempo for each movement. Better to perform your reps slowly than fast, especially if you find yourself using momentum to lift the weight. Muscles are built by stimulating the fibers and corpuscles with *applied resistance,* not by jerking, swinging, tossing, heaving, or bouncing the bar into orbit. Every gym has one fellow who cheats wildly on every exercise he does (and it is always a he—women are just not so ego-oriented). Everything he does is epitomized by bounces, tosses, leans, and squirms. Sometimes he even yells to draw attention to himself. Ugh! This man is the ugliest trainer imaginable. Watch any exercise he does and you will see how *not* to train a muscle. His face shows a

Nimrod King pumps his incredible biceps with the single arm pulley apparatus.

Perhaps we'll never know who's behind the massive Mike Quinn physique.

Gary Strydom and Bertil Fox.

pained expression from the first rep. But look deeper. This person does not have much to offer in the muscle department either. No wonder. He hardly works his muscles. Certainly he never performs a full-range movement. Nothing is ever done slowly. And no way is he ever going to make an exercise harder by concentrating and *feeling* the muscle contracting.

Here is a suggested mass-building routine. Note that it is limited in length and variety. But it works.

MONDAYS, THURSDAYS

Eight Minutes Assorted Abdominal Exercises

Press behind neck	5 sets	8–10 reps
Squat (to bench top)	5 sets	10–15 reps
Bench press	5 sets	8–12 reps
Parallel-bar dips	5 sets	8–10 reps

TUESDAYS, FRIDAYS

Eight Minutes Assorted Abdominal Exercises

Wide-grip chins	5 sets	12 reps
T-bar rows	5 sets	10 reps
Calf raise	5 sets	15 reps
Leg curls	5 sets	12–15 reps
Barbell curls	5 sets	8–10 reps

Give the above routine time to prove itself. Results don't all come in a week!

After three months on this routine, you may want more variety. The following is a more comprehensive mass-building routine. Again, it's not overly long, but brevity is the name of the game when mass is the number-one objective. Split the following routine in any way you wish, as long as each exercise is performed twice weekly.

Eight Minutes Assorted Abdominal Exercises

Prone hyper extensions	5 × 15
Press behind neck	5 × 8
Seated dumbbell press	5 × 8
Squat	5 × 12
Hack slides	5 × 15
Thigh curls	5 × 12–15
Calf raise	5 × 15–20
Bench press	5 × 10
30-degree incline flyes	5 × 10–12
T-Bar rows	5 × 10
Chin behind neck	5 × 12–15
Barbell curl	5 × 10
Incline dumbbell curl	5 × 10–12
Lying triceps extensions	5 × 10–12
Triceps pulley pressdowns	5 × 12

Few people can fly with this much weight. Ali Mala shows how!

Luiz Freitas showing the pain of training the calves.

5

INCREASING PAIN TOLERANCE

Easing Achievement

How good are you at tolerating pain? Your answer may be the key to your success or lack of it! Let's face it: bodybuilding can be so physically demanding that it is actually painful. And if you allow pain to keep you away from your workouts, naturally your progress will suffer.

I watched Reg Park, multi–Mr. Universe winner, training in England in the early fifties. He was around twenty-four years of age. I was immediately struck by his tenacious attitude toward his workouts. Yes, he was in pain, but he would not give in to it. Thirty years later I read an account by writer M. McFarland in *Muscular Development* magazine. The subject was Reg Park's visit to Hawaii. Here is what McFarland wrote: "In Hawaii several years ago Reg was up late past midnight practically every evening. Nevertheless, he would arise at 5 a.m. and go to the gym to train, doing many sets of heavy front squats or some other equally rugged workout.

His extraordinary capacity for dedicated purposeful activity was evident. Reg had developed a high pain tolerance." This rang of truth: I had noticed this same lack of concern for pain in Reg when he trained in his youth. McFarland continued: "Reg's experience of discomfort was undoubtedly compounded by very little sleep, a hectic schedule, social commitments and really rugged workouts, yet he persistently refused to submit or compromise with the natural inclinations towards laziness."

Recently I photographed Reg Park, incredibly now at the age of *sixty*, almost forty years after having first watched him train in England, at the World Gym in California. He raced through over twenty sets of curls, twenty sets of triceps work, fifteen sets of calf training, and fifteen sets of thigh training. He paused only long enough to let his son Jon-Jon perform his set, but frequently they would train in unison, and then the between-set rest would be less than thirty seconds. But what made this training quite incredible was that Reg, at the age of sixty, was handling some pretty hefty poundages.

Arnold Schwarzenegger is another individual who doesn't give in to pain. Even if he has only had a few hours' sleep the night before, he will still be up early, training as hard as anyone else. He has a self-commitment to train, and nothing gets in the way.

Bill Pearl is another. He still trains at four in the morning. However busy or tired, Bill doesn't miss workouts. He once said, "If a person can't find a couple of hours a day for himself, then something's wrong. I take care of my own workout needs first in the morning. After that I can think of other people, business and social commitments."

Now, have you noticed a connection between these guys? Each served in the military. Park and Schwarzenegger were in the army, and Pearl had enlisted in the navy. Each went through basic training, which, among other things, teaches self-discipline and tolerance for pain. Whatever conclusions we draw from this link between all three men, I think we can safely surmise that military training didn't harm their attitude towards gritting their teeth and getting the job done.

Short of joining the army, what can you do to develop an iron-clad will and a tolerance for painful exercise?

One answer is to develop a true vision of what you want to achieve. When you know, *really* know, what you want from bodybuilding, then the actual execution of steps to achieve that goal are easier. When you have faith on your side—the utter conviction that come hell or high water, you will succeed—then expect that nauseating pain to subside.

Most of us have natural rugged good health, but a small proportion of the population are not so lucky. They have a poor tolerance, not only for pain, but for strenuous physical exercise. If

Canada's John Cardillo works on the lateral raise machine.

Gary Strydom works on the lateral raise pulley.

such is the case, then you cannot expect to keep pace with Park, Schwarzenegger, or Pearl. It's a physical impossibility. Also, though somewhat unlikely, you may have some undetected physiological malfunction. If you have any reason to suspect this, see your doctor. Explain your passion for bodybuilding and have a thorough physical checkup. Once you get the go-ahead from your doctor, you will feel better mentally — secure in the knowledge that you can apply yourself fully to hard-core training.

Are you missing workouts right now? Or cutting them short because of pain, laziness, or general discomfort? What about your personal habits?

SMOKING

Cigarette smoking kills a workout. Few of the name bodybuilders smoke cigarettes, and those who do fail to make the big time. Every cigarette has over 200 poisons in it. The heavier and longer you smoke, the more damage these poisons do to your system. Not only are you flirting with lung and throat cancer, but you are also increasing your chances of heart disease, emphysema, and circulatory problems. Smoking does not marry well with activities like bodybuilding. Weight training tests the pressure on the walls of veins and arteries, and smoking contributes to the premature hardening of these same blood transporters. You could blow a fuse.

The short-term effects of smoking are shortness of breath and acute fatigue. Both drain your energy tremendously and rob you both of the will to train and the ability to follow through physically if by some chance you can fool yourself into taking a workout.

DRINKING

Like smoking, excessive alcohol consumption is a drain. Doctors tell us that a drink (or two) a day is A-okay, but beyond that we should not go. Many find that drinking before a workout makes them sleepy. Others say their mental tenacity and resolve to train hard is diminished if they drink prior to training. Since alcohol is a sedative, it

Ahead of his time.
Reg Park at twenty-four.

lessens the pain of exercising, but it also interferes with form and technique. You need a clear mind to train correctly, and alcohol does not contribute to this condition. Needless to say, the long-term effect of heavy drinking is devastating. Not a few promising bodybuilders have fallen afoul of this disease.

NUTRITION

Another cause of low pain tolerance is poor nutrition. Make sure you are eating foods from the various food groups:

- *Milk* (milk, yogurt, cottage cheese, and cheese)
- *Meat* (beef, veal, lamb, pork, fish, poultry, eggs)
- *Vegetables* (fruit, vegetables, legumes, nuts)
- *Grains* (whole grains, cereals, bread)
- *Fats* (butter, margarine, oils)

About 70 percent of your diet should be made up of grains, fruit, and vegetables; the remaining 30 percent should come from the milk and meat groups.

One sure way to invite poor health is to feed yourself junk foods that don't have any real nourishment. You can't live healthily on hot dogs and fries, cookies, coffee, and candies. Make a habit of eating wholesome foods that are relatively untouched by man. Fresh fruit, vegetables, lean meats, whole grains . . .

Start your day with a good breakfast, including a large bowl of grain cereal (oats), fresh fruit, and yogurt. Follow that with a couple of boiled or poached eggs, some wholewheat bread, and a glass of milk. A good breakfast will *set up* both your attitude and your energy levels for the balance of the day. Proper nourishment will keep you nutritionally safeguarded from deficiencies, some of which make us unable to tolerate normal pain levels. Some of the best foods for keeping healthy nerves intact and maintaining proper levels of pain tolerance include whole grains, nuts, bananas, citrus fruit, and organ meats such as liver, kidney, or heart. McFarland

himself is a strong believer in linoleic acid in maintaining the ability to handle stress and physical pain: "It stimulates the growth of intestinal bacteria and helps to produce the indispensable B-vitamin complex."

A POSITIVE ATTITUDE

Develop a positive attitude toward your training. Use it to combat laziness. If you find that you are starting to consider missing a workout, flip through a couple of bodybuilding magazines. Ogle the pictures, see the rippling muscles; tell yourself over and over, *That's the way I want to be.*

Another way of beating the workout blues is to mentally prepare yourself prior to training. An hour before, get yourself in the mood. Go through the exercises in your mind. Reassert your goals. Visualize your dream body. Set new rep targets in some of your exercises. Use every trick in the book to drum up enthusiasm.

Arnold Schwarzenegger works hard on barbell curls.

Standing thigh curls as performed by Shawn Ray.

6

ONE-SET TRAINING

Fact or Fallacy

It's that old intensity factor again. The advocates of the one-set-per-exercise system base their opinion on so-called scientific findings which supposedly show that a muscle can be maximally stimulated from just one all-out set of high-intensity "progressive resistance" exercise. This philosophy was pushed mainly by two Iron-Game personalities — Arthur Jones, inventor of Nautilus, and Michael J. Mentzer, Mr. Universe — both of whom believed in heavy, all-out, controlled (very strict) reps. Each man had mastered the art of inspirational writing. They expounded their ideas graphically, with such conviction that in the seventies and early eighties the whole bodybuilding world was trying their methods. El Darden wrote books on high-intensity. Mike Mentzer made a zillion selling "heavy-duty" courses and videos propounding the method. Art Jones promised *Iron Man* readers that just one all-out set on Nautilus exercise machines would take bodybuilders to the Mr. Universe level in double-quick time. We all gave one-set training our best shot. Virtually every champion tried it. Norm Zale, Chicago's superexpert on matters of bodybuilding

and diet, told me that a club where he worked had some 16,000 members, and all the *serious* hard-core trainers were using the heavy-duty technique. "These people have learned to train with amazing intensity," says Zale, "yet they are not growing. Some are actually shrinking from nervous exhaustion. When you train all-out over a period of weeks and months, you run the risk of working more than your muscles. You may be draining your nerve resources. Very few bodies indeed can cope with adrenal exhaustion, which is a by-product of constant heavy-duty training. Personally, I have not seen one heavy-duty trainer build appreciable muscle size or strength from one-set training."

I myself have to admit that I did make some progress using all-out intensity, but I quickly came to a sticking point where further progress was impossible. The benefits of this form of training are, first, that it is extremely efficient as a time saver. You don't spend hours in the gym when following this method. Second, one's gain in pure force (strength) is evident. When you go all-out for a lift, you are challenging the muscle

Heavy-duty giant Mike Mentzer takes his own medicine on the dumbbell curl exercise.

to get stronger, or else. But even strength progress comes to a halt if it is forced rather than coaxed. In truth, as muscle size and strength levels approach their natural limits, some high-intensity methods have to be employed, but these cannot be strung out over a long period of time without inviting burn-out.

Mentzer and Jones would often claim that bodybuilders who used five or six (or more) sets per exercise were wasting their time and that they should stick to just one or two sets of all-out effort and then move on. At the height of the hype, Larry Scott publicly pointed out that he had always used high-intensity training, including forced reps, isotensions, and burns, but he also believed in doing more than one or two sets. He used five or six for every exercise, and, yes, as one who witnessed some of his many, many workouts, Scott did go all-out on each and every set. Tom Platz is another who applies more of Mentzer's heavy-duty effort than Mentzer himself. And Platz does eight sets for each exercise.

But let's look at how most champions train. Scott and Platz aside, most use all-out effort infrequently. But if you look into their past, there have been times when they have used high-intensity principles (negatives, forced reps) to reach a new plateau, and even today they will use these methods now and again. What you will *never* see is a true champion training off-season (not for an upcoming event) who uses high-intensity methods on every exercise.

Here comes a bombshell: *Most championship-caliber professional bodybuilders train with moderate weights, using three to four exercises per body part, four to six sets per exercise, utilizing eight to twelve reps, and each muscle group is trained twice weekly.*

Bruce Page calls this pumping, but to me pumping is using very light weights for sets of twenty reps or more. Pumping is something you do backstage, before competing, to temporarily enlarge your muscles. Right now Lee Haney, or Mike Christian, or Rich Gaspari, could drum up a huge pump by doing a quick set of fifty push-ups, but it wouldn't help one bit toward building mass. I call the champions' way of exercising . . . *quality training.* It runs smoothly; the tempo

is perfect. There are no long conversations, no heaving up of the hips in bench presses, or bouncing out of the squat. A champion trains with the mind set on the job at hand. Concentration is tuned in to steel-trap accuracy. There is a mind/muscle connection that can be cut with a knife. Sure, there's an attempt to add weight to the bar now and again, but it's a secondary consideration to making the muscle *feel* the action. *You can't get the feel of an exercise if you have to concentrate on lifting the resistance.*

Now, having said that, let's admit that the muscles do occasionally cry out for some strength movements. Moderate weights lose their appeal, pumping is out of the question, so we are left with the prospect of "going heavy" for a while. This practice will definitely bolster muscle strength, ligaments, strength, and powerful joints. Confidence too may be lifted. The important thing to remember when throwing in a few heavy low-rep movements after training conventionally for a period is that you go heavy only on certain exercises. It is most definitely *wrong* to use megaton poundage on isolation exercises like thigh curls, triceps stretches, concentration curls, or any uni-joint movement. Save your heavy stuff for multijoint (combinational) moves like squats, bench presses, T-bar rows, press-behind-neck movements, or parallel-bar dips. Keep this kind of strength training to just a few weeks, or alternatively go heavy on the bench press or squat once or twice a month just to keep in touch with the feeling of power.

Getting back to the one-set principle. *It doesn't work.* It will not make you a champion. It has never worked, and never made a champion.

As you may know, a muscle cell contracts fully or it doesn't contract at all. The aim when weight training for mass is to get as many fibers to contract as possible. One all-out, heavy-duty set will contract a lot of fibers, but it doesn't compare to the amount of fibers broken down with six sets of slightly less intensity, so long as there is a regular effort to increase resistance on a steady basis.

The proponents of heavy-duty will tell you that one or two sets of super-intensity are better

Larry Scott works his biceps on the bench that carries his name.

than *any* number of sets with lesser exertion. Their reasoning is that the using, say, of 150 pounds in an exercise set after set does not increase the resistance, and therefore your muscles are not learning to use more weight and will not get bigger. My contention is that with every successive set you *are* breaking down more cells, and if you are minimizing your rest between sets, each and every set *will* become harder to perform. *You are indeed breaking down more muscle cells.* And, more important, you are doing it without earth-shattering intensity effort that makes your face turn so purple and your veins almost explode from the pressure. And you know why I'm right? Because the bodybuilding world has tried heavy-duty. They believed in it, they gave it their all, and they failed. Musclebuilders today who hold the top titles are training with conventional methods utilizing plenty of sets and reps, because they have tried heavy-duty and not made sufficient progress.

Back in the fifties, a former editor of the Weider magazines, *Mr. America* and *Muscle-*

Builder, Charles Smith, says there is nothing new under the sun when it comes to strength training and bodybuilding. For the most part he's right, but there are a few new angles, Charles. Forgive me. In all the books I have written on the subject, I have always made a point of introducing some original thought, and I have never missed out on bringing something entirely new to the readers.

Let's face it—Arthur Jones's Nautilus ideas were new. He used a cam to tailor the resistance to the body's strength curve. My own Pre-Exhaust invention was new. Not one hint of the method appeared before I released my findings in 1968, and Arthur Jones himself used the principle in his Nautilus machines. Powerlifting body suits are new; the whole array of modern supplements and drugs (heaven forbid) is new. Pek Deks, cable crossovers, computer exercise apparatus, muscle videos, and fat-free female bodybuilders are new . . . and, believe me, we are only just beginning.

In fact, bodybuilding has advanced so much in the last forty years that there is absolutely no

Tom Platz giving everything to the thigh curl exercise.

doubt that the winner of the *women's* nationals today would have been a *unanimous* winner of the *Mr.* Universe contests of the forties and fifties. That's how far we've come.

Writer Joe Miller of Ocean, New Jersey, has addressed the issue of one-set, heavy-duty training as opposed to multiset training. He concludes: "The bottom line is that there seems to be some discrepancy between what is being advocated by the one-set brigade and what the human body can physiologically handle and benefit from. Can a normal human being equipped with average recuperative powers withstand the amount of stress that is imposed by all-out intensity training? The adrenal glands undergo great change and break down after just two or three weeks. Then everything else is set up for failure. Single-set-training advocates preach . . . maximum effort all the time. My suggestion is use it only occasionally and for short periods. Most workouts should be based on the multiple-set method."

Heavy dumbbell shrugs form a part of the
Bob Jodkiewicz workout program.

Lee Haney working on hack slides.

Mike Christian in a rare moment of relaxation.

Gladys Portugues strikes an amazing pose.

WORKOUT CYCLING

Pushing to a Peak

Building your body is like a journey. Naturally, you will want to complete the task as quickly as possible, but like any long journey you will have to pace yourself. Making your way from A to B is seldom done best by pushing at your outer limit all the time. This is what cycle workouts are all about. Best results come from carefully planned pushes to the top, followed by periods of lesser intensity. Watch a baby's first crawling. You will see that there are big pushes followed by comparative rest. Like a baby, you too need to consolidate your efforts to move to the top of the bodybuilding ladder.

Frank Zane was the first of the modern bodybuilders to follow the cycle-training principle. He called his plan *phase training.* He was the most organized trainer of his time. Typically, Frank would start his system in January after taking a rest from heavy bodybuilding during October, November, and December. During these fall and winter months, Frank would ride his bike, swim, scuba dive, and shoot archery. Come the new year, he would slowly start up with his weight workouts. He would never force himself

to go to the gym. He worked out only when he had a genuine urge to do so.

These early training sessions would be basic. A few movements only; no record attempts or a harnessed rush between sets. Gradually, as his enthusiasm climbed, he would allow order to return to his training, more exercises crept in, and, by the end of this first cycle he would be training every section of his body at least twice weekly. Frank Zane would keep to this initial phase for approximately three months, building up his training poundages, gradually adding a few exercises, but keeping well within his limits in both the length of routine, time spent in the gym, and amount of intensity applied to his efforts.

Somewhere in the first week or two of April, phase two is put into action. This is where Frank gets serious. Each body part is now allocated a proper balance of exercises. Weak points are given additional attention. Sets are added and rest time between those sets is diminished or limited to little more than a minute. Most important, intensity is increased to a high level. By the beginning of May, Frank Zane is really rollin'.

Amazing Canadian André Maille.

Multi-Mr. Olympia Lee Haney stretches before his workout.

Phase three is started in July, and it's time to get selfish. Zane turns in on himself and concentrates solely on self-improvement. This is the time when he takes in extra sun, when he practices his posing, studies himself in the mirror, concentrates on perfecting his exercise form. . . . He gives no seminars or guest appearances.

During phase three Frank increases his intensity even more. He adds workout days. He begins to drop high-calorie foods, lowers his fat and sugar intake. Rest periods between sets come down to a mere thirty seconds. He is totally *into* body improvement at this stage. Conversation in the gym never exceeded a grunt. No phone call will reach him. . . . He is aiming for his annual peak.

This has been Frank Zane's habit since around 1965. It has won him more contests than he has kept record of, including three consecutive IFBB Mr. Olympias. Today Frank still follows this pattern of training even though his competition days are over. He likes to aim for peak condition each fall.

In one of my routines on bodybuilding I wrote, "There's an old saying which you are sure to hate. In addition you will hate me even more for suggesting it. It has no place in a publication dedicated to musclebuilding.

"The saying? Ah, yes: *Make haste slowly.* The ironic thing is that if you push, push, push in your workouts each and every session, you will drive yourself into a sticking point."

Zane knows this. All the male and female pros know it. And now you know it. *Any condition that you can maintain year round is not a peak condition.* Far better to push hard, harder, hardest . . . and then withdraw. Zane peaks just once a year. It was always that way with him. Most top bodybuilding pros feel the same way. Some, however, manage to peak two or even three times a year, but in truth it's a great effort; an ordeal invariably for the ego-primed young lions of the sport. Let me say here and now that there are bodybuilders who go all-out every workout, who never give less than their best. My own observation about these trainers is that they are young and enthusiastic, so full of ambition that

Mr. Proportion, Frank Zane.

they just do not burn out mentally.

Cycle training is usually performed by older, more experienced bodybuilders who in their youth may have blitzed and bombed every workout, but who today find that they get best results from intelligent cycle-training. Offhand I would say that most professional men and women bodybuilders cycle-train whereas most amateurs do not. Only the toughest of the tough can drive themselves at full throttle all year. It usually comes down to this. You have to cycle-train or take occasional layoffs.

Boyer Coe feels that layoffs are counterproductive. He claims that the Soviet philosophy of taking "active rest" is far superior. Getting back to Zane, even in his rest phase (prior to phase one) he would involve himself in sports and pleasurable physical activities. This is his active-rest period.

It's interesting to note that some bodybuilders cycle their training from workout to workout. In other words, they will perform a light workout once in a while. They may use the same weights, sets, and reps, yet use only 90 percent of their regular poundage. This of course should not be confused with feeder workouts (see the chapter on that subject). Feeder workouts involve only a few sets of high "pumping" repetitions to keep the blood "feeding" the area.

One form of cycling I call the *carry-along principle.* Select a couple of body parts that are somewhat below par; your weak areas. . . . Design your routine so that these areas are really bombed hard with additional exercises. Add more sets. Hit the muscles from a variety of angles. Now, because you are adding more time to your routine, you will have to perform fewer sets and exercises for your other body parts. Fine. That is

Marjo Selin.

Harry Dodich working on barbell curls.

Shane Dimora stretches out on the leg-extension machine.

the plan. You add work to boost your weak areas and reduce work on your stronger body parts, but you still perform enough to keep them big and strong. You *carry them along* while you blitz the want to change your routine to blitz another couple of areas. See where the cycle principle comes in? The message remains. You can't blitz and bomb *all* your body parts *all* the time, so you have to specialize on one or two weak areas and keep the others up in size with a minimum number of sets to maintain the status quo.

There is little doubt in my mind that cycle-training is good for you. After training for a peak, gradually building up your poundages, number of exercises, workout frequency, and intensity for a particular contest, it is a good idea to rest up somewhat by changing your exercise habits and downgrading your training intensity. Pro body-builders will frequently take up less strenuous activities such as sailing, bike riding, or swimming, all with one aim: to allow the body to regenerate. This comparative rest provides a sound base from

which you can ultimately proceed to a new cycle of increased intensity to reach a new plateau of muscular glory.

Of course a bodybuilder who hasn't won or even entered a show would not necessarily aim for peak competitive condition until he's ready to actually enter a contest. Consequently, there hasn't been that superstress that a contest-peaking bodybuilder undergoes, and accordingly there is no need to wind down by reducing your exercise to sailing and Ping-Pong. Keep to your weight training, but always be aware that some form of cycle-training is advantageous. When you deliberately hold back in your workouts you are leaving something for tomorrow, and because you have paced your progress, held back that fraction of a percent, a new plateau of development will assuredly arrive. Harness your enthusiasm and control your workouts. You will be surprised at how you can still use high-intensity progressive training even when you don't go all-out in every set. It will work for you.

Larry Scott trains on the hack slide machine.

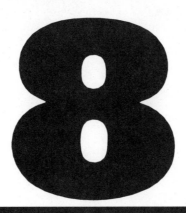

8

CUTTING THE TEMPO

Breathtaking Performance

Human beings want success. And they want it yesterday. Impatience is one trait that many of us share. We don't want to wait forever for our achievements. We want it all; and we want it now!

Ask a typical bodybuilder which factors contribute to achieving extra muscle mass in the quickest time possible and you will invariably be showered with a dialogue including sets, reps, poundage, sequence, exercise style, frequency, concentration, and training intensity. Chances are one of the most important factors, *time,* would be completely overlooked. I'm not talking about the amount of time it will take before you walk from that distant stage clutching your first Olympia trophy, nor am I talking about spending more time in the gym. Just the opposite. I want to point out the importance of cutting your rest time between sets. This is another way of increasing intensity. It's been scientifically documented. It's not a matter for conjecture. It's a fact. The less rest you take, all other variables being equal, the

faster your muscles will be growth stimulated.

Needless to say, if you have been treating yourself to five-minute rests between your exercises, it will be neither practical nor useful to suddenly reduce your rest time to thirty seconds between each set. You have to make reductions in rest time . . . a gradual procedure. Rush it and you'll be inviting mission impossible to your workouts. You could even cause your progress to stop, or even worse . . . to regress.

Reduce your rest time by just a few seconds to begin with. Cut a few seconds every workout. Ideally you should aim for thirty seconds' rest between sets of most exercises. You might want to rest up to two minutes on heavy exercises like back squats, but on other leg movements such as hacks, thigh extensions, and leg curls you should still be aiming for that thirty-second target. Theoretically, a thirty-second rest may sound too long, but let me assure you that if you are training with exercise style that really challenges

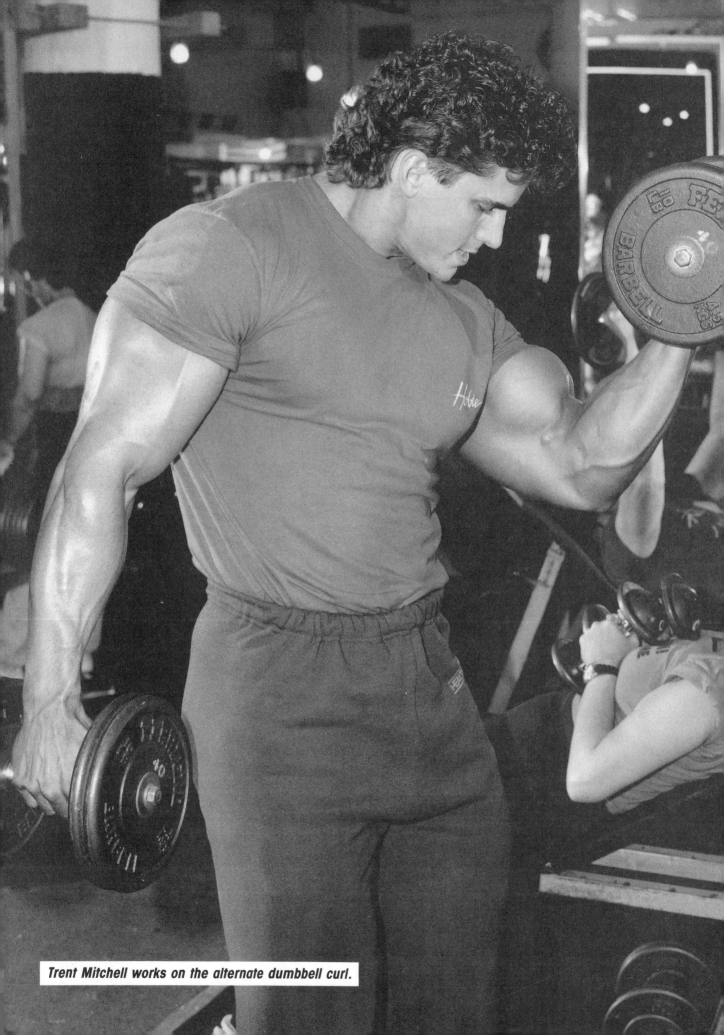

Trent Mitchell works on the alternate dumbbell curl.

Working one arm at a time for his shoulders. Serge Nubret.

your muscles, and if you are using weights that make you work like you've never worked before, you will need that thirty seconds' relaxation between your sets. There are advocates of taking even less rest, and, true enough, a very fit person can take just ten seconds' rest or even less, but this always entails a reduction in exercise poundage. An interesting fact to know is that a muscle recuperates about **90** percent of its strength within the first four seconds of rest, but a heck of a lot longer is needed for that same muscle to recover **100** percent of its original strength.

The idea of reducing rest time is not new.

Anita Gandol performing the triceps pressdowns exercise.

Harry Dodich.

Vince Gironda wrote about it and used the principle over thirty years ago. And, yes, Vince was one of those who advocated trying to reduce the rest period to ten seconds or less between sets. Vince understood the basics of increasing intensity more fully than anyone in his era. Do most bodybuilders use this rest-reduction technique? Yes, but it is utilized to its fullest around contest time. Six weeks prior to competing, most aspiring men and women start to really cut their between-sets rest time. This is also advocated so long as the weights are not swung up and down. When you use momentum to complete a repetition, you are definitely cheating yourself.

Another early advocate of reducing rest time between sets in order to increase the muscle-building effect is Serge Nubret of France. At one time Serge could squat with over 600 and bench press a cool 500, but in the late sixties he totally reversed his training philosophy and spent more time concentrating on the muscle itself, improving exercise form, using isotension and, yes, minimizing rest time between his reps and sets. Particularly the latter. Serge would use about eight sets per exercise and would constantly aim to perform all eight sets in record time. This became very important to him when training specifically for a contest or a guest posing exhibition.

The usual barometer of when to train on another set has been the breath factor. In other words, people would go to a subsequent set when their breathing had returned to normal. This is still a good method for beginners to follow.

For those who want to embark on using less rest time to improve their training progress, I suggest you take note of how much rest you usually take and then systematically try to lower it, always keeping within your level of personal fitness and ability to tolerate strenuous exercise. Do not cut more than a few seconds at a time, because this can cause your oxygen debt to interfere with your ability to complete a set. For example, imagine you are performing the squat exercise. You do a heavy set of fifteen reps and your chest is heaving up and down to gulp in much-needed oxygen. Should you start the next set within ten or twenty seconds, it will be useless to your legs because your need for oxygen will literally prevent you from continuing to exercise. In other words, your lungs will give out well before your legs are fully stimulated. You'll have great cardiovascular efficiency, but your leg mass won't be impressing too many people. Too much too soon could also cause you to throw up simply because of overstressing the system.

Bruce Page, a close friend of mine and a man who has written more bodybuilding articles than any other living human being, is an ardent believer in reducing rest time as a means to increasing muscle mass. Listen to his pronouncements on how to perform the barbell curl: "Place a barbell on the bench press racks. Use a poundage that will enable you to perform ten reps, with the last two or three taking a little effort to complete. Take a wide grip, but keep the elbows as close to the sides as possible, and perform your first ten reps. At the completion of these place the bar back on the racks, breathe deeply, and *rest for ten seconds only.* By the time the ten seconds are up, the bar should be back in your hands."

A problem of reducing rest time exists if you enjoy using one-arm movements such as the single leg curl or extension, single-arm presses, single-arm lateral raises, dumbbell triceps extensions, or concentration curls. Obviously a set lasts more than ten seconds, thus the free limb gets to rest for up to a minute or more. In this case I simply recommend that you speed up your reps to the max and take no more rest than is employed while changing the resistance from one limb to the other.

Of course training techniques such as supersets or the Pre-Exhaust method demand that rest time be minimized, but this chapter is designed to stress the importance of minimizing rest time during the performance of straight sets.

Off-season training by its very nature is slower and more controlled than pre-contest training, but even so you will benefit by reducing rest time to around that sixty-second mark. This is known as quality training. And aside from helping you build more muscle, there is an additional benefit. You'll complete your workouts in a shorter period of time. That's not so bad, is it?

Gary Strydom performing cable crossovers for his chest.

Colossus Mike Quinn concentrates in the mirror on his triceps pressdown.

FEEDER WORKOUTS

Prolonging the Pump

If you asked 10,000 bodybuilders what a feeder workout is, I bet 99.9 percent of them wouldn't have a clue what you were talking about, which is strange, considering that feeder workouts are one of the most effective ways to speed up muscle growth, especially if you have reached a sticking point in your training.

Do I have your interest? Just what are feeder workouts and how can they improve your training? A feeder workout is a light, high-rep, low-set, low-intensity, pumping workout done for a muscle group at a training session separate from the main regular workout (usually the day after). So, in fact, you are training the same muscle group two days in a row. The purpose of the feeder workout is not to severely work the muscle again or to try to tire it out and break down more tissue, but to remove waste products from the muscle, and, most important, to nourish or "feed" it with rich blood. Thus the term "feeder" workout. The feeder workout aids in tissue repair, improves blood circulation, and increases recovery ability, thus greatly enhancing conditions for growth.

The idea of feeder workouts is not new. People have been doing them for over thirty years. And many of the top champions of the past three decades have at one time or another done feeder workouts (or a variation of the feeder-workout principle). They may not have even known they were doing feeder workouts, or if they did, they may not have known all the technical and scientific reasons for doing so, but, instinctively, they sensed it was the right thing to do. Because it works!

Back in the 1960s, Dan Mackey, a Vince Gironda follower, used to advocate doing forearm work the day after biceps workouts. Dan believed that the blood pumped into the forearms fed the biceps, too, and greatly increased biceps growth. Even today, Vince Gironda himself will sometimes give hardworking bodybuilders workouts for the same muscle group two or even three days in a row, with the second or third workout being a feeder. Don Howorth, just back into heavy training these last couple of years at Vince's, is reportedly doing feeder workouts for his thighs and reporting great gains.

Marjo Selin and Carla Dunlap.

Former Mr. Universe Ricky Wayne, who sported some of the biggest arms in bodybuilding in his day, used to do three sets of fifteen reps of cable curls and three sets of fifteen reps of one-arm cable triceps pressdowns on his off-days to maintain his arm pump. It was one of Ricky's secrets, and except for Larry Scott, nobody had better arms at the time.

Currently, Marjo Selin, the great woman bodybuilder from Finland, trains her biceps and triceps on different training days. But on biceps day, Marjo will add a couple of sets for her triceps, and on triceps day she adds a couple of sets for her biceps. She finds this greatly aids in recovery and helps to promote growth.

Let's get into some of the technical reasons why feeder workouts work and some of the theories that support the idea of feeder workouts.

In bodybuilding and weight-training, the pump (getting a lot of blood into a muscle) is of paramount importance. Since the blood is the only means of transporting material to the muscle and removing waste products produced by exercise, it stands to reason that anything that increases blood supply to the muscle will result in faster gains. In other words, the more blood flow, the more potential muscle mass.

In order for a muscle to grow, it basically needs three things:

1. It must be stimulated to grow via some kind of overload (heavy workout),
2. It must be given the opportunity to grow by providing the right conditions for recovery, which will allow it to grow, and
3. It must be provided with the protein and

nutrients it needs to repair and enlarge (muscles are made from amino acids with the help of enzymes called ribosomes. The ribosomes are activated to that duty by messenger RNA).

Just because you have done a heavy workout to stimulate growth in a particular muscle group does not mean it will necessarily grow if the conditions are not right for growth. The stimulation provided by a heavy workout is, by itself, not normally enough for growth to occur. Unless the muscle can recover and rebuild before the next workout, it will not grow bigger or stronger. Heavy training provides the stimulation necessary for growth, but makes inroads into your recovery ability. As well, the heavy workout breaks down a lot of tissue, depletes ribosomes and messenger RNA, and clogs the tissue with lactic acid and other waste products. While these waste products are essential for rebuilding the muscle and rebuilding ATP stores in the muscle (essential for energy and muscular contraction), if left in the muscle too long, they can hamper recovery and slow progress.

Increasing recovery ability, then, is ultimately just as important for growth as the growth stimulation from the heavy workout. There are many factors involved in promoting recovery ability, but we are going to concern ourselves with only one: improving blood circulation to the muscle, to feed the muscle. Increasing blood circulation will build more muscle. Frequent pumping of a muscle increases blood circulation and thus increases recovery. That is why the veins grow larger as you train — to facilitate greater blood flow to your muscles.

If pumping is so good, why not just pump all the time? Well, some people can and do. Serge Nubret and Freddie Ortiz, for example, found that all they ever had to do to grow big was lots of sets, lots of reps, and pump, pump, pump. But these people are genetically superior types who can grow muscle tissue, replenish carbohydrate stores, and recover at the same time. But most people, due to low hormone levels and poor or average genetics, just cannot stimulate muscle growth without high-intensity and/or heavy training.

At the same time, most people who do just heavy training usually don't recover well enough to promote growth. So pumping is needed to feed the muscle and promote recovery. The more you pump, the more the body is able to respond to the stimulus from the heavy training. According to researchers, circulation to a muscle can be increased an amazing fifty times normal! This means that pumping a muscle regularly can also increase recovery ability up to fifty times normal, too, depending on the amount of pump achieved.

So we can agree that pumping is needed for optimal growth. But the question is not how much pump, but *when* to pump for best results. This is related to the waste or fatigue products that are produced in the muscles when weight training.

Back in the mid 1970s, Dennis DuBreul wrote a series of very interesting and informative articles for *Iron Man* magazine. In these articles, DuBreul put forth his theories of what has to take place for a muscle to grow and how to optimize muscle growth. He came up with what he called the fatigue product theory, which makes a lot of sense to me. The theory is that the waste or fatigue products produced by a contracting muscle directly stimulate growth of the muscle and are essential for the rebuilding of cratine phosphate stores and ATP stores. According to DuBreul, these various fatigue products all have different chemical duties and functions and must be allowed to remain in the muscle for a certain amount of time. If he is correct about these fatigue products playing a key role in the rebuilding and recovery of muscles, it stands to reason that if the fatigue products are flushed out of the muscle immediately after you exercise, the muscle will not recover and rebuild to the extent it would if the fatigue products were allowed to remain in the muscle. And, at the same time, if the fatigue products are left in the muscle too long, they can hamper recovery or at least slow progress. So, for optimal results, the fatigue products can't be flushed out too soon or left in too long.

But the trouble is, most people do one or the other. Either they don't remove waste products and bring in nutrients fast enough to support recovery from their heavy workouts, or they remove them before they have stayed in the mus-

Laura Beaudry concentrates on the wide-grip dips for chest.

Mohamed Makkawy performs bench dumbbell rows.

cles long enough to perform their very essential chemical duties. And while it would seem ideal to train very heavy during a workout to stimulate growth and then immediately follow up with some lighter pumping to promote recovery, DuBreul thinks this is wrong. He believes the minimum time fatigue products must stay in the muscle to perform most of their duties is about twenty minutes. Ideally, you would train only one muscle group, wait about twenty minutes, then start another muscle group. Immediately training a new muscle group diverts blood to the new muscle group being trained and removes the fatigue products before they have done their vital jobs.

I recommend waiting twenty minutes between muscle groups to take advantage of the fatigue-product theory and then doing the light, pumping feeder workout the next day. This way you know all the chemical functions have been performed, and the feeder workout will remove the waste products and bring in fresh, rich, nutritious blood to aid in recovery and growth. Vince Gironda subscribes to this theory as well.

But remember, these feeder workouts must be very light and should not tax the muscle at all. You are just trying to increase blood circulation to the muscle without tiring it out. One to three sets of fifteen to thirty reps with weights that are 20 to 30 percent of your normal is plenty. So, for example, if you normally use 225 pounds for your bench presses for ten reps, then for your feeder workout you might want to use less than 100 pounds for twenty reps. Likewise, if you normally do dumbbell curls with 50-pounders for eight reps, then 15-pounders are all you will need for a biceps feeder workout.

You don't necessarily have to do feeder workouts for each muscle group, but if you do, I would start with only one set of thirty reps and work up to three sets. I recommend that you do feeder workouts for any muscle group that is just not responding as you'd like it to. As well, I would recommend that you take advantage of the fatigue-product theory and train that muscle group alone, by itself. That way you can train it when your strength and concentration is highest and the fatigue products will remain in the muscle a long time.

A key point to remember. Obviously, if you expect to nourish your muscles with the blood you pump in, you had better be eating properly to ensure nutritious blood. When going for maximum growth, Arnold Schwarzenegger always advocated $1\frac{1}{2}$ to 2 grams of protein per pound of body weight. Eat plenty of meat, fish, poultry, eggs, and milk, as well as lots of vegetables, fruit, and some breads. Each day try to eat foods from each food group to ensure a balanced diet.

Take your supplements, too. Free-form amino acids have revolutionized bodybuilding. They allow you to get plenty of protein without too many fattening calories and no stomach bloat. As well, they keep your blood sugar up and keep the body in positive nitrogen balance. You might want to try the Vince Gironda method of taking three to five amino acid tablets every couple of hours to keep the body saturated with protein.

Liver tablets are time-proven and are a good supply of protein, minerals (especially iron), B vitamins, and the energy factor P-450. They also keep blood sugar levels elevated, keep you in positive nitrogen balance, and contain an antiestrogen factor. Again, try taking three to five every two to three hours along with the free-form amino acids.

A good milk-and-egg protein or egg-protein powder will supply you with extra calories and protein if you are trying to gain muscular weight. As well, you should take a good high-potency vitamin-mineral tablet, extra vitamins A, C, D, and E, plus some kind of germ oil for a supply of unsaturated fatty acids.

Vince Gironda has recommended taking 400 mg of the amino acid lysine with meals for every 100 mg of protein. Vince is also big on raw glandulars and raw orchic and recommends these supplements along with other supplements to "tune up" the body's chemistry.

A method Don Howorth used to increase his capacity for pumping was to take the following supplements one hour prior to training: 200 mg of iron, plus B vitamins and B-12, copper, chlorophyl, wheat germ oil, and amino acids. He would follow this for several weeks and then back off on the supplements, especially the iron. Don truly felt that doing this increased his vascular capacity and aided his ability to pump up. And he was famous for being able to just blow up like a balloon from the pump he achieved.

If you find that your time is limited and you cannot take twenty minutes between muscle groups, try to train muscle groups that are close to each other, like traps and delts, or pecs and delts, biceps and triceps, calves and thighs. This way the fatigue products will remain in one area of the body. What you don't want to do is train two body parts that are not closely situated. Work one small area of the body and then let the whole body rest for at least twenty minutes.

On the other hand, if you have lots of time to spare, try training only one muscle group per workout. Arnold and Franco Columbu, Mohamed Makkawy, Vic Downs, and more recently Serge Nubret and Al Beckles use this method a lot. In fact, Nubret will sometimes bomb one muscle for an hour and then fall asleep right in the gym for an hour or so, before moving on to a different body part. Beckles will usually train one muscle very hard in the morning, go home to sleep, and then come back to the gym at night to train a different muscle group. The results speak for themselves.

Give feeder workouts a try. You're sure to see improved results from your training.

10

STRENGTH

Setting the Stage for Basic Gains

Training for strength and training for muscle size are entirely different. This used not to be the case. . . . In years gone by, muscle size was merely a by-product of hoisting huge weights. But gradually, as the sports of bodybuilding and powerlifting grew apart, two distinctive training philosophies developed.

Today strength athletes and bodybuilders train differently, think differently, eat differently, and even recuperate differently. Since for the most part we become good at what we practice, bodybuilders gain more shapely muscle mass, and strength athletes get stronger. This isn't to say that lifters don't build some mass or that bodybuilders don't gain strength . . . but these things are only accidental by-products of their training focus.

It therefore may come as a surprise to you when I tell you that weightlifters can occasionally use bodybuilding methods to help their lifting progress. And, yes indeed, bodybuilders can benefit from periods of specific strength-training to help their musclebuilding progress.

When weightlifters and powerlifters use supplementary bodybuilding exercises, they do more than help their appearance. They build the muscle and tendons from a different angle, and because of the higher reps, they generate better blood supply and improve the nerve pathways to the muscles themselves. Conversely, the bodybuilder who occasionally uses low-rep strength-training techniques can quickly strengthen the tendons and ligaments, thus increasing overall strength and the ability of the body to handle heavier workloads when training with higher repetitions. This results in more muscle size.

Strength training also brings its own rewards. The ability to lift heavy weights, though not a requirement in bodybuilding competition, does give the trainer a higher self-esteem. It's nice to be as strong as you look!

The philosophy behind building body mass is to trick the body into thinking it has to build more muscle. This is done in a variety of ways. Bodybuilders will perform many sets of an exercise, and they train each body part with three, four, or even five different movements. Rest time between sets is diminished so that the muscle is kept in a constant state of pump. Most important, the mind is called on to heighten the muscle-

Fullest concentration is given to the curls of Mike Christian.

Few train harder than multi-Olympia Lee Haney.

building effect. Exercise style is combined with the deliberate squeezing of the muscle to force an exaggerated intensity into the area, thus creating a trick effect to induce the body's mechanisms to call for added hypertrophy (muscle mass).

Weightlifting and powerlifting are simpler pastimes. That is not to say that they are easier. They are not. It's just as difficult to become a powerlifting champ as it is to get to the top of the bodybuilding ladder. But the philosophy is more basic. While observing the rules of each lift, one merely strives to lift a weight from A to B.

"If you want to get big and strong fast," says Mike Lambert, editor of *Powerlifting USA* magazine, "the answer is to use the basic heavy exercises. Nothing does the job better." The following is a routine of basic-strength exercises that you may wish to adopt for a ten- to twelve-week period.

Press behind neck
1 × 12, 1 × 8, 1 × 5, 1 × 3, 2 × 2
Squat
1 × 15, 1 × 10, 1 × 6, 2 × 3, 1 × 2
Bench press
1 × 15, 1 × 8, 1 × 6, 3 × 3, 1 × 2
T-bar rows 1 × 15, 1 × 12, 1 × 8, 3 × 6
Deadlift 1 × 8, 1 × 6, 2 × 4, 2 × 2

When training for strength, one is at a greater risk of injury, but if you observe the rules of warming up with a set or two of higher reps, and keep the bar in the same groove when using heavier weights with lower reps, you will reduce the chances of injury.

PRESS BEHIND NECK

1. Experiment with various grip widths, but keep in mind that the best grip width is probably one where the forearms are vertical while the upper arms are parallel with the floor.
2. Make sure you always use a spotter on your heavy sets, even though you may be using support stands.
3. Never use a "false" grip. The thumb should always be curled around the bar to lock it into position, to avoid slippage.
4. Before taking the weight to start the press-behind-neck motion, double check that your upper back is flat, your head up, your lower back arched with the glutes projected out and back.
5. Lower the bar at a moderate speed between reps. Do not drop it quickly or bounce from the traps. Do not lower too slowly because of the possibility of burnout.

SQUAT

1. Adopt a basic position suited to your body type. Feet should be facing out slightly to an angle. Use built-up shoes or a wooden block if there is difficulty with balance. Individuals with long legs frequently require added height under the heels.
2. When the squat is performed, it is important that the thighs take the major load of stress. If you find yourself leaning way over (and rising with your head between your knees), too much stress is being placed on the hips and lower back.
3. Hold the bar high on the traps when squatting. Keep the back flat and the head up. Keep a tight grip on the bar.
4. Always keep control of the weight when you descend into the squat. Absolutely no ballistics or bouncing from the low position.

5. Use spotters when squatting with heavy weights. Make sure they know exactly what to do if you get stuck in the low position. Getting stuck with several hundred pounds on the bar is no joke!

BENCH PRESS

1. Stabilize yourself by keeping your hips, back, and head on the bench. Be sure that your feet are symmetrically placed, flat, to balance the body during the movement.
2. Do not use a thumbless grip, where fingers and thumbs are at the same side of the bar (false grip). It has to happen only once and you could be injured for life . . . or worse.
3. Never drop the bar to the chest to jet the weight upward. You risk injury to the rib cage and you also rob the muscles of important stimulation. Lower the weight at a moderate pace.
4. At the conclusion of the lift, do not slam the bar back into the racks. You could (a) sever a finger, (b) tip the bench backward, (c) miss the racks completely and have the weight crash down on your body.

T-BAR ROWS

1. Possibilities for lower-back injuries are increased with this exercise. Keep the back flat and head up throughout the movement.
2. Angle your torso to the correct plane that gives you the least lower-back stress. If you feel a "twinge" in your lower back, stop performing the exercise immediately.
3. Make sure that the arms are fully straightened and the lats maximally stretched at the bottom of each rep. Start the pull slowly, resisting the temptation to jerk the weight up.

Luiz Freitas performing preacher bench curls.

DEADLIFT

1. Starting position is critical. Make sure that the hips do the lifting. Keep the back flat and the head up throughout the movement.
2. Never bounce the weight up from the floor, platform, or boxes . . . start the lift with one hand overgrip and one hand undergrip . . . slowly.
3. If you have a problem gripping the bar during the deadlift, then use heavy-duty training straps to "cement" your hands to the bar. Never drop a deadlifted weight—lower it lightly to the ground.
4. Do not practice heavy straight-leg dead-lifts. This is inviting lower-back problems. The exercise may be done, but not with heavy weights.

Strength training differs from most body-building training in that exercises are done slowly. The focus is solely on getting the weight up. *Not* on stimulating, fatiguing, or destroying the muscle. Powermen rest more between sets; five minutes is quite common. Repetitions for strength building are never above six. World bench-press champion Ted Arcidi, who has officially benched 705 pounds, likes to train using six reps, but he will also concentrate on twos and threes as a powerlifting meet approaches. Ironically, Arcidi does not like to perform "singles," but most strength athletes will test their best single attempt once every two or three weeks. Too-frequent attempts at a single repetition can lead to an overtraining condition or burn-out.

Progression is extremely important in any type of strength training. You cannot play with poundage. *When you are on a drive for strength, you have to add weight to the bar.* It's a good idea to keep a record book and jot down every lift that you do. (When strength training there is plenty of time between sets.) This practice will keep you up to date on where your training is going, and there will even be enough information to allow you to decide *when* you need to reach for that new plateau. Keep a record of your nutritional, supplemental, and recuperation habits also.

Upright rows as performed by Californian Scott Wilson.

Strength-training workouts usually involve only a few exercises. Even our suggested routine in this chapter should be divided into two or three parts. Train each exercise only twice weekly. Even at this you will not be able to go all-out on every workout. Powerlifting champs who train on each movement twice weekly have only one *real heavy* session per week. If we train superhard on a strength exercise (with low reps) more than once a week, we will be inviting a burn-out situation.

Joe Bucci adds a little weight to the 45-degree leg-press machine.

Jim Quinn relaxes in Gold's Gym, California.

Michael Ashley and Shane Dimora.

11

TESTOSTERONE

The Multipurpose Hormone

What is testosterone and can it help the body-builder? Testosterone is the male hormone, and, yes, a good supply of it does help your body-building. Both men and women have levels of circulating testosterone in their blood. And both sexes also have estrogen, the female hormone, in their systems. As one might suspect, men have considerably more testosterone than women, and women have substantially more estrogen than men.

Testosterone is a remarkable substance. Not only does its use as a "supplement" contribute to more "masculinity" (i.e., muscle size, strength), but there are unwanted side effects, especially in the long term, of baldness, acne, deeper voice, heightened aggressiveness, liver problems, increased likelihood of heart attacks after middle age, and of broken-down immune systems. All bad, bad news, you'll agree.

Curiously, testosterone is responsible to a great degree for our sexual desires. When levels are high, both men and women feel more like participating in sex, and they enjoy it more too. And they say there's no such thing as an aphrodisiac? For years scientists thought that it was the female hormone which helped "lure" women into being more receptive to sexual encounters. But no. It has now been concluded that both males and females are most sexually active when their testosterone is synchronized at high levels. It has also been determined that testosterone levels in males can rise at the time when the testosterone levels in females are also high (at ovulation — about midcycle). It has been hypothesized that the scent of the ovulating female triggers a rise in the male's hormone level. This is not to say that any two people of the opposite sex will fall into each others' arms if they both happen to have high testosterone levels. Our actions are still governed by our minds: married couples or steady partners will be more likely to copulate than casual acquaintances, since their libidos will be in tune with each other.

Testosterone has been used by chemical manufacturers in the production of *synthetic anabolic steroids.* These carry the same side effects, though to a lesser degree, as testosterone. Scientists found that they could alter the basic structure of the testosterone molecule to produce a safer drug, but one that was by no means free of serious side effects, especially when taken in high dosages over long periods. Anabolic steroids do add muscle size in both men and women bodybuilders. They do add strength. They do add almost miraculous hardness. They allow you to train harder and longer and recuperate better. They even serve to help chase away fat from the body. If they weren't so very dangerous they would be labeled miracle workers. They are not worth the risk.

I have observed bodybuilders change their personalities by taking steroids. I have seen normal, likable men turn into monsters of aggression. Numerous bodybuilders have ended up in trouble with the law as a result of starting fights or because of unprovoked aggression. Some have even beaten up their wives. All because of steroids.

Sometimes you read in the press about the violent actions of famous heavyweight athletes . . . football players, weightlifters, bodybuilders, and wrestlers . . . they make the news over a fight or some other altercation. . . . Again, let me venture to suggest that in most cases it was steroids that made them do it.

Statistics have shown that people in prison for violent crimes have far higher testosterone levels than those who were imprisoned for fraud or other nonviolent crimes. I'm not saying that these convicts were steroid takers, merely that they had naturally higher levels of the male hormone.

Testosterone is often referred to by fitness experts as being the reason why men can de-

Show those triceps. John Hnatyschak, Steve Brisbois, Shane Dimora.

Matt Mendenhall,
one of the greatest of all.

T-bar rows are part of the Gary Strydom workout.

Dumbbell rows as demonstrated by Shawn Ray.

velop big muscles and women cannot. Many women have pretty high testosterone levels, naturally, and they manage to gain a considerable amount of muscle. But it is indisputable that women who take steroids are able to gain more muscle mass than those who do not. It is, however, not suggested that women take steroids because of the potential risk of masculinization of the voice and facial features, loss of head hair, development of facial and body hair, enlargement of the clitoris, and even cessation of the normal menstrual function. Additionally, there are unknown factors involving pregnancy. There is evidence that a female fetus could develop secondary masculine characteristics . . . there is also a possibility that babies born to steroid-taking parents may not have the normal immunities of other children.

When steroids were first developed around 1938 (testosterone was around in the late 1880s and administered to the superwealthy in Switzerland as a youth serum), they were used to help the aged recover from debilitating operations. They were also given to burn victims and later to war casualties. Reportedly, German soldiers were given steroids to make them more aggressive in battle.

Today steroids are still legitimately used in hospitals to help weakened patients gain mass and strength, but by far the greatest percentage end up being taken by athletes, weightlifters, wrestlers, and bodybuilders to help them win titles or trophies. Have you ever watched top female athletes compete? Haven't you ever wondered why so many look like men? Regrettable as it is, women at the top of almost every sport have had to resort to drugs. Women runners, swimmers, gymnasts, field athletes, tennis players . . . take steroids. They want to win, and in order to do so they will do almost anything. Remember that question fielded at the 1976 Montreal Olympics: "If you could take a pill that guaranteed a gold medal at these Olympics, yet which caused you to die a month later, would you take that pill?" A massive 60 percent opted for the pill.

Yes, there is drug testing at the World Bodybuilding Championships and at the Olympic Games. And that testing is as thorough as they can make it. But it doesn't stop those with a burning desire to win. They either halt their drug taking a short time before the testing or they beat the test by other means. Women, for example, have been known to insert a catheter containing normal urine (i.e., from a person who hasn't been taking drugs) into the vagina. Then, when the compulsory urine test is made, the "clean" urine is squeezed out into the test bottle. Men have gone so far as to have drug-free "clean" urine injected into their bladder minutes before being tested!

Well, what's the bottom line on steroids? We know they are used by strength athletes and even swimmers, cyclists, boxers, sprinters . . . but should a bodybuilder use them? For me, this is the most difficult question to answer. I am not a steroid user. I am not a doctor so I cannot give a qualified medical opinion. I do know that large doses are potentially dangerous. I do know that long-time use of even moderate amounts of steroids is unhealthful and even life threatening. I do know that steroids, when combined with good nutrition and exercise, even in moderate use give an almost instant hardness to the body and an increase in muscle mass that can't be equaled without their use.

I have observed that heavy steroid takers get hooked on the feeling of being bigger and stronger, and are loath to give up taking them.

I have also noticed that heavy users spoil their bodies with these drugs. Large amounts of steroids bunch up the shoulders, increase the likelihood of serious injuries (often leading to irreparable tears and rips), enlarge the midsection area (everything grows, even the intestines, which enlarge and push out the waistline to barrel-like dimensions).

My only way out of this is to tell you the truth about steroids, which I have done, and to suggest that taking them is not a smart move, since there is so much that is negative about the practice.

Fabulous Penny Price.

Mike Quinn.

12

THE ETERNAL QUESTION

Gaining Muscle While Losing Fat

Yep! It's the most-asked question of all. How can I gain muscle while losing fat? Some say it can't be done. It can be accomplished, but it is harder for some than for others. I might as well come right down to the bottom line. Those who take anabolic steroids find it comparatively easy to gain muscle mass while losing fat. No, I'm not recommending steroid use. I'm just stating a fact.

For the rest of us, it's a matter of adopting a carefully balanced diet. We need to feed the muscles sufficiently, allowing enough extra ingredients into the system to add muscle, yet not so much that there is a surplus to add fat. It is a precarious balance, so much so that the Iron Guru, Vince Gironda, insists that his pupils don't even try to gain muscle and lose fat at the same time. "I tell the fatsoes to lean out first. Get the adipose off," says Vince. "And then they can start building lean muscle from scratch."

Uppermost in importance when trying to gain muscle and lose fat is that you don't ingest empty calories. No sugar or sugar-loaded foods . . . cut

out those cakes, cookies, chocolate, candies, soft drinks, gravies, fried foods, butter.

Get them out! Keep your foods based around fresh fruits and vegetables, lean meats, fat-free milk, cheese, yogurts. . . . Bake your potatoes (no sour cream), steam your vegetables, and eat your fruit raw. Bread and cereals should be wholegrain. Nuts should be unsalted. Follow my recommendations and you will be on the right track. I should add here that when you base your food intake around fresh fruits and vegetables, you will not have much of a problem with fat unless you have an inherited predisposition to fatness or if you suffer from a glandular malfunction.

I do not agree with counting calories. For one thing it's impossible. No one can count the exact number of calories they take in, and certainly no one can tell you how many calories you need to gain or lose weight. You must go by *feel*. To lose weight you should reduce your calorie intake gradually. When you start losing one or

Janice Ragain.

two pounds a week, you know you have hit the right amount of food (calories). If you are losing too fast (no energy, loose skin, drawn face), take in a little more food. With diligence you will find the right balance. But you do have to eat intelligently. You cannot afford to eat emotionally, nor can you pander to the whims of appetite and taste.

Fat has such a bad name in our society that we tend to forget that it is a very natural phenomenon, and a necessary one. Fat cells are a natural part of our body makeup. They insulate organs such as the heart, kidneys, and liver. Fat lubricates joints and buffers between skin and muscle. Fat is also your supply of emergency energy when glucose may not be supplied. Glycogen (from glucose at 250 calories per pound) supplies our short-term energy needs. Fat (at 3500 calories per pound) provides energy for more prolonged activity. Women have naturally higher fat percentages than men (36 percent). Men average 23 percent. Both are too high. Average is not normal. My recommendation is that men strive to hold an average body-fat percentage of 12 to 15 percent, while women strive to maintain an average of 20 to 25 percent. It's been concluded by the medical experts that men need only 3 percent body fat and women 6 percent to maintain normal body functioning. To the eye, this level of fat would make a subject appear *extremely* defined. Ideally, one could be forgiven for thinking that bodybuilders should try to hold body-fat percentage at these levels, or just slightly above these figures . . . but theory doesn't easily pan out in reality. Your personal fat-levels are frequently tied in with genetics. Some people naturally carry more fat than others. *Excess* fat levels, however, are seldom

World Gym, Maui: Bob Jodkiewicz goes all-out on the seated rows.

Steve Brisbois performs triceps dips.

inherited — they are usually the result of too much of the wrong kinds of foods and too little of the right kinds of exercise. Each of us is born with a predetermined number of fat cells, and these increase in size rather than in number, although babies and young children, if overfed, can increase their *number* of fat cells. If you were a fat baby, there is a reasonably good chance that you have more than your fair share of fat cells right now. That translates to your ability to carry more fat than others on your body. It may be harder for you to get truly *ripped* than another bodybuilder who was not an overweight baby or who didn't have overweight parents. This is not to say you will always be fat, but merely that you will be inclined toward a "thick skin" that is hard to truly define come contest time.

Training to increase muscle size while losing fat must be controlled in both intensity and duration. Workouts should be approximately the same length and similar in their overall demand on your body. Inconsistent workouts will cause your body to hold on to fat. Now is not the time to surprise your body with shock tactics or sudden excessive workouts. Likewise when it comes to nutrition. Set a standard pattern of regular food intake so that the body's internal clock can hone in on your eating habits, trust them, and give up fat stores because it can rely on regular fuel coming in from your set eating times.

My suggestion is that while you are on this special campaign to increase muscle while losing fat, do not adopt any specialization programs, Pre-Exhaust, supersets, forced reps, burns, giant sets, or anything else excessive. Train using the regular *set-system*. Exercise each body part twice

Larry Scott works on the horizontal bar with a special ab twist exercise.

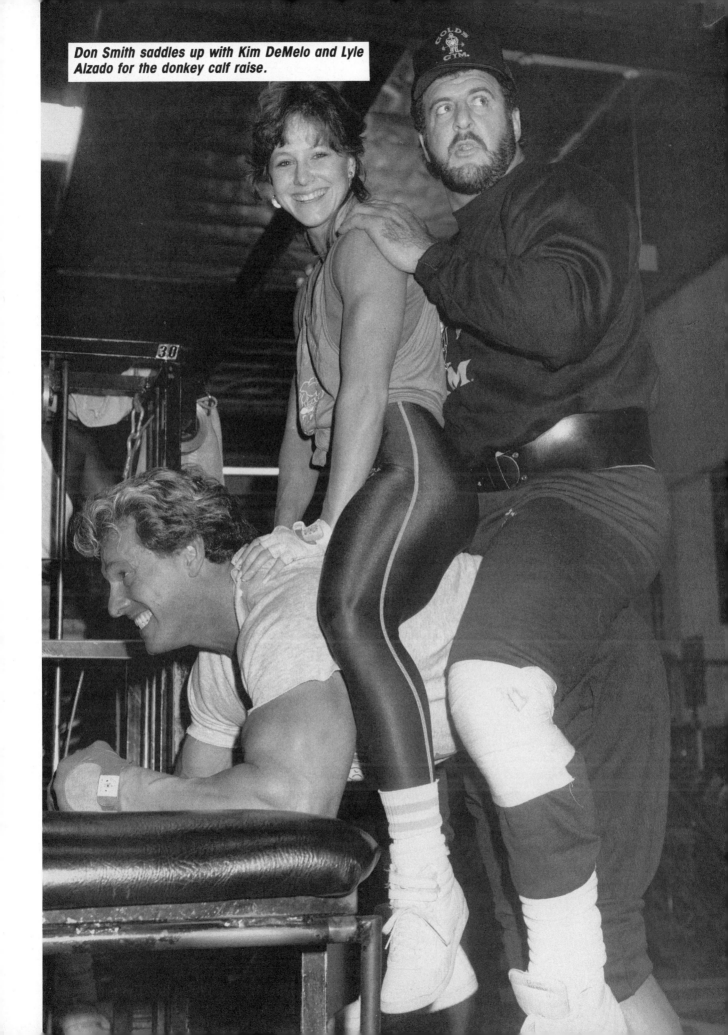

Don Smith saddles up with Kim DeMelo and Lyle Alzado for the donkey calf raise.

Ali Mala performing incline bench presses.

Joe Bucci works on the press behind neck.

weekly and keep your workouts to approximately 1¹/₂ hours each. Add poundage only when it is indicated. Do not allow yourself to get locked in to an *increase-weight-at-all-costs* situation. Don't misunderstand me. You must train hard, but at this time your workouts should not be either irregular or excessively demanding.

The following is a good example of what I'd consider an ideal routine. Remember that changes in number of sets may have to be tailored to your individual fitness level and personal tolerance for strenuous exercise. It is also recommended that this routine be split into three roughly equal workouts.

EXERCISE

Chest

	Sets	Reps
Bench press	5	6–10
Flat bench dumbbell flyes	5	10–12
Incline dumbbell bench press	5	10

Upper Legs

Squat	5	10–15
Hack machine squats	5	12
Thigh extensions	5	12
Thigh curls	5	12–15

Shoulders

Press behind neck	5	6–8
Upright Row	4	10
Lateral Raise	4	10–12
Bent-over flyes	4	12–15

Abdominals

Hanging leg raise	4	12–15
Crunches	3	15–20
Side twists	3	50–100

Lower Legs

Standing calf raise	5	15
Seated calf raise	4	20
Leg press toe raise	4	25

Back

Chin behind neck	5	10–15
T-bar rows	4	10–12
Seated cable rows	4	12
Prone hyperextensions	4	12–15

Forearms

Reverse curl	4	15
Wrist curl	4	15

Biceps

Barbell curl	4	8–10
Incline dumbbell curl	4	10
Seated concentration curl	4	12–15

Triceps

Close-grip bench press	5	10
Lying triceps stretch	5	10
Triceps pressdowns	4	12–15

Talk about balance. Roy Callender of Barbados adopts an unusual pose.

13

SNACKING

Grazing for Physical Culturists

No more three square meals a day! Nutrition experts are giving the seal of approval to something bodybuilders have been advocating for decades . . . snacking. But though the process is the same, the name has changed. No longer is this system of having six or seven "meals" a day known as snacking. The *in* word today is "grazing."

The idea behind recommending three square meals a day was to completely satisfy the body's need for food and then allow a four- or five-hour break from eating. It was believed that this was the best way to avoid digestive problems, by giving the system a rest. But modern science, working hand in glove with nutritionists, now feels that smaller, more frequent snacks put less stress on the digestive system than three large meals. So snacking is in. A new grazing era is upon us.

Bodybuilders wishing to gain weight have always been encouraged to eat five or six meals daily. This not only prevents overloading the stomach, with its attendant problems of indigestion, bloat, and laziness, but it also ensures that the muscles have a pretty constant supply of food on hand to maintain nourishment for their every demand.

Today, however, nutritionists are declaring that this same snacking procedure used by bodybuilders to gain weight is also ideal for people who want to lose it. As you might guess, the only difference would be in the proportions of each snack. A 220-pound man wishing to pack on mass will invariably be enjoying larger (and possibly more frequent) snacks than a 110-pound woman yearning to lose ten pounds of excess flab. But the principles are the same. Divide your daily allocation of calories into five, six, or seven equal-sized mini-meals.

Having said that, I will offer a slight contradiction. *Make breakfast your biggest meal of the day.* You will feel better for it. Ironically, most people, bodybuilders or not, make breakfast their smallest meal. Some of us misguided souls only gulp down a couple of mouthfuls of coffee before scrambling out the door en route to our jobs. If you have fallen into this syndrome, then I implore you . . . Go to bed that little bit earlier and get up in time to have a decent first meal of the day. You will feel great all day long if you follow this bit of advice.

The following are a few sample grazing-diet suggestions. I have listed actual amounts, but of

course this is up to you because overall calorie requirements vary according to sex, age, fitness level, weight, and activity level. Also bear in mind that assuming you are holding a steady weight at present, you will need more calories to gain weight and fewer calories than you are now consuming to lose weight. Please note that the foods I recommend are wholesome and nutritious. I suggest you try to avoid man-made junk foods as much as possible. I'm aware that we have no alternative but to eat out of a vending machine on occasion, or at a fast-food restaurant, but keep these times as rare as possible. Junk food is not good for you and will not help you reach your long-term goals.

Women on a special diet may have to reduce their daily calorie intake to 1000 a day, or even slightly less, but do remember that losing weight is best done at a steady pace of losing no more than two pounds per week. Do not try to lose more than this. Heavens, it translates to over 100 pounds a year anyway. By the same token I have known men who require 7000-plus calories a day to gain size. So you see, it's all relative.

I don't really suggest that you attempt to count your precise calorie intake. For one thing it's impossible. Who's going to tell you exactly how many calories there are in a big apple . . . or a small tomato?

I have, however, listed the approximate calorie content of the foods in my suggested menu. This is to act as a guide only. You should learn which are the high-calorie foods and which are the low ones. For this reason it might be a good idea to buy a calorie counter or small booklet

BREAKFAST

Meal One

	Calories
1 cup oatmeal or rolled oats	130
1 tbsp. raisins	80
2 tbsp. bran	33
1 1/2 cup raw whole milk	225
1 sliced apple	100
Meal total	**568**

MID MORNING

Meal Two

1 carrot-raisin muffin	85
1 1/2 cups milk	225
1/2 grapefruit	45
Meal total	**355**

LUNCH

Meal Three

	Calories
3 oz. cold, sliced lean roast beef	250
1 oz. Cheddar cheese (1″ cube)	116
2 carrot sticks	20
1 slice wholewheat bread	72
1 medium tomato	35
lettuce (2 leaves)	20
1 large glass water	
Meal total	**513**

MID AFTERNOON

Meal Four

1 cup fruit salad (No sugar. Any combination of strawberries, tangerines, peaches, bananas, blueberries, raspberries, grapefruit, apples, pineapple)	80
1 1/2 cups whole milk	225
Meal total	**305**

DINNER

Meal Five

Fresh vegetable soup (1 bowl)	100
Salmon steak (6 oz.)	300
Brown rice (1/2 cup)	100
Broccoli (2 stalks)	90
2 broiled tomatoes	70
Coffee (black)	
Meal total	**660**

EVENING SNACK

Meal Six

2 oz. unsalted cashews or peanuts	200
1 bran muffin	85
1 cup plain yogurt with tangerine slices	190
Meal total	**475**
Meal Total for the Day	**2876**

showing the calorie contents of various foods. There's no harm in having this information at your fingertips. For example, those trying to gain weight will find it useful to know which are the highest-calorie foods. And those wishing to lose weight can snack on low-calorie items like celery or carrot sticks, or fruit and salads. You will note that in my suggested menu I have still kept to the traditional breakfast, lunch, and dinner format, with additional mini-meals thrown in. Truthfully, this isn't pure grazing. You can of course make all your meals snacks and discard the traditional names. There is no real reason why we should breakfast on eggs, lunch on salads, or dine on steak.

It is very important that you plan snacks ahead of time. Whether you are a student, teacher, laborer, truck driver, or office worker, you cannot rely on getting a good snack simply on the off chance that it will be available when and where you want it. Snacking has to be thought out in advance. Prepare your snack at

home. Not only will you be eating the best foods, you will be eating the correct amounts and proportions.

Although you may be able to buy the odd apple or orange, coffee-truck food is no good. Most canteen food is bad. Fast-food establishments are usually poor, and vending-machine food is atrocious. If you don't have access to good nutrition at work, prepare cold cuts, cheese, salads, and fruit. I find a sectioned-off plastic Tupperware dish to be very useful. These dishes are airtight, so a degree of freshness is preserved, and food doesn't get mixed up on the way to work.

One of the all-time favorite foods of bodybuilders is tuna, of which there are many varieties. Most of us prefer the white; others don't mind the dark. But your main concern should be whether or not it is based in water or oil. Beware! Oil contains loads of calories. Just a tablespoon of oil (or butter or margarine) provides about 100 calories.

If you want to gain weight quickly, tuna packed in oil is for you, not just because of the added calories, but because it also contains more nourishment; the protein content is higher, for one thing. But if you are cutting up for a contest or some other special occasion, there is only one tuna for you, the water-packed variety.

Another ideal snack is poultry. Chicken and turkey are white meats low in fat. They have less fat than hamburger meat, which is a good reason to eat them, whether you are trying to gain or lose weight. Make sure your chicken is cooked thoroughly: some chicken has been found to be contaminated. If limiting yourself to poultry sounds too restricting, then by all means eat red meat, but trim the visible fat away before eating.

Cheese is a good snack food but it is not suitable for those trying to lose weight. It contains way too much fat and accordingly does not help the dieter's quest for lower body fat (remember, fat builds fat). Even cottage cheese is not the ideal food for a person wishing to lose weight. True, it is lower in fat, but it is also very high in sodium (salt), which causes the body to retain water under the skin.

Lance Dreher.

Tony Pearson poses for the lens of MuscleMag *International's Steve Douglas.*

Luiz Freitas.

Beautiful Clare Furr works her delts with the lateral raise movement.

Beautiful Marjo Selin spots husband Hannu.

Harry Dodich performs incline dumbbell press.

14

PROTEIN

How Much Is Right?

Protein seems to be back in favor. Make no mistake — for a while protein was most definitely persona non grata. It's making a comeback, however. This, despite a recent study I came across which indicates that any intake in excess of ten grams at any one sitting will result in a gain of fat. (I often wonder whom they studied to arrive at that figure — twelve-year-old, seventy-pound gymnasts in the off-season, no doubt.)

These days the big thing is again high-protein intake, based largely on Soviet findings of strong correlations between increases in strength and dietary protein. Claims both for strength and intake are frequently enormous.

So should you increase your protein?

Maybe.

First let's go back to the beginning. It was in the fifties that the first direct correlation was drawn between protein and lean muscle tissue. It seems so obvious now, and it was probably instinctively understood then, that muscle is composed of protein. After all, when you eat a steak, what is it? Cow muscles. But it was about that time that a definitive analysis was made of the actual composition of muscle tissue. Know what the primary ingredient was? Nope, wrong. It's water. About 70 percent. Most of the rest

was protein, with lipids (fat), trace amounts of minerals and such making up the rest. Now everyone knew that taking in extra water wasn't going to give you muscles (unless you lifted very heavy glasses), so the fixation went to the protein. Was that a reasonable leap of logic? Maybe.

So for a long time everyone ate protein, and the beef industry was grateful. Then someone took a long look at the above-mentioned muscle analysis and fixated on the water and said, well, hey, maybe that protein stuff ain't so hot after all. I don't know who originated the idea, but I can tell you who its major proponent was. Any of you who have been in the iron game for any length of time will remember Mike Mentzer. Mike was (is) an incredibly gifted bodybuilder now retired from competition. He was very probably the most scientific bodybuilder of his era, and arguably the most genetically gifted. Mike's basic attitude was that if you divide a year's worth of gains into the days of the year, the amount of protein needed to make those gains was virtually nonexistent. Ten pounds of pure muscle in a year, a respectable gain, works out to about twelve grams a day of muscle. If you figure that 70 percent of that is water, then your muscle gain required fewer than four grams of protein

Cable laterals demonstrated by England's Frank Richards.

Mike Quinn.

beyond maintenance levels. So you consume only moderate amounts of protein, making up the rest in complex carbs to give you the energy for high-intensity training to make the most of the protein you consume. Pretty compelling argument, especially when you looked at Mike. Now, Mike wasn't one of your assembly-line creations. God himself took a personal hand in his genetics. He could have gotten enough protein from a diet of cardboard to look absolutely awesome. The rest of us need some help. My problem with the above line of reasoning is that it assumes too much. It assumes a lot about what a maintenance level is, what kind of efficiency is involved with conversion of dietary protein to usable lean mass, the quality of protein consumed, and how well that protein is assimilated.

More and more, in recent times, that line of reasoning isn't being followed. As I said, protein is becoming popular again. I've heard recommendations in excess of two grams per pound of body weight. God help any bodybuilder with a predisposition to gout on a program like that! Excessive protein intake puts a strain on the system, particularly the kidneys, whose role is to filter all the uric acid. Anyone consuming a lot of protein should also increase his water intake. Protein is a lousy energy source. Its only real role in the body is cellular synthesis. Go beyond that and you can't just burn off the rest as you would with a carbohydrate; it becomes fat.

So, OK, how much?

Well, I can't tell you.

See, I'm going to take a new approach. Or maybe it's the oldest approach of all.

I guess the problem is that everyone would still like to think of bodybuilding as an exact science. Back in the twenties and thirties, everyone did three sets of ten, three times a week, and that was that. Pretty soon athletes came to realize that people responded differently to different levels of training, and now we have training routines as divergent as imagination allows. Why is it that people are still trying to do the old-fashioned thing with nutrition? Everyone's different. My protein requirements are different from yours, are different from Arnold's, are different from his lovely wife Maria's. For optimum re-

sults there's no question you'll have to establish your own personal requirements just as you've had to figure out how many sets of bench presses you need to work your chest best.

Your first obstacle is in knowing how much you're currently getting. I'll bet not one in ten of you really knows. How much protein was in that turkey sandwich you ate for lunch? How much in the omelet you had for breakfast? Here are some figures for you:

3 oz. cooked hamburger	21 grams
3 oz. broiled steak	20 grams
1 oz. Cheddar	6 grams
3 oz. broiled chicken	20 grams
3 oz. leg of lamb	22 grams
2 oz. beef liver	15 grams
2 cups cooked beans	29 grams
8 oz. skim milk	9 grams
4 oz. salmon	32 grams
4 oz. tuna	32 grams
5 oz. baked ham	33 grams
24 large shrimp	33 grams
4 eggs	26 grams

See how much food you have to eat to get the level of protein some of these Soviet studies are requiring? The only calorie-efficient way to do it is with a protein supplement. A couple of tablespoons in skim milk would do it for you.

The next problem is assimilation. The textbooks always said the human digestive tract can't assimilate more than 25 grams in any three-hour period. This is an accepted limitation. It's no coincidence that most every protein powder has on the label a recommended dosage somewhere in the vicinity of 30 grams. It also means that by that guideline it's impossible to consume more than about 180 grams per day. Figure it out, you run out of hours.

Well, I've got a problem with that one too. Anytime the books say something about human physiology as a hard-and-fast rule, it should probably be trashed. Especially where bodybuilders are concerned. A top-level bodybuilder can do things without batting an eye that would kill an average person. (If that sounds like a ridicu-

Lee LaBrada.

Rick Valente works his biceps on the Scott bench.

Joe Bucci.

Horizontal curls as performed by Berry Demey.

lous exaggeration, why not grab a guy off the street and put him in front of a squat rack with 600 pounds on his shoulders and yell "*squat!*" Tom Platz could do it twenty times.) What I'm saying is that any limitation that applies to average humanity doesn't apply to strength athletes, and that includes protein consumption. If 30 grams is the limit for a statistically average male of 154 pounds, but you weigh 200-plus . . . well, you figure it out.

There is one limitation that no amount of training will probably alter, and that's the frequency with which protein can be consumed. The standard rule used to be three hours. Now it seems that synthesis of pepsin, the enzyme primarily responsible for protein digestion, needs anywhere from four to five hours to be fully activated. That means at least a four-hour wait between protein doses. You might be able to reduce that with the ingestion of proteolytic (protein digesting) enzymes such as papain or bromelain with each meal.

OK. So how do you know how much protein you really need? How do you go about tailoring a personal dietary intake? Well, it's safe to assume you need at least the RDA. That's .36 grams per pound or .8 grams per kilo of body weight. If you're a two-hundred-pounder, that works out to 72 grams. Start there. Allow yourself a minimum of six months to really give yourself a chance to properly evaluate your performance levels. Then increase by, say, 10 to 15 percent and try for another six months. Take your time. How long did it take to find the optimum training program? Heck, you're probably still working on that one. I know I am.

Keep increasing protein intake for as long as you continue to show positive improvements from it. You'll know you're overdoing it by several indications. When you stop seeing substantial size and strength improvements. When you feel bloated much of the time (an indication that you're overloading your digestive capabilities). When you get fat. Too much protein is as bad as not enough. Just like training.

Now some words about water intake. Protect your kidneys. Drink enough. Not just for your kidneys' sake, of course—you're a water-based creature; not much of anything works at peak efficiency if you're low on water. Also, don't lose sight of the fact that muscle is 70 percent water. So how much do you drink? I know the books say eight glasses a day, but you know what I think of the books. Besides, what's a glass? Eight ounces? Six ounces? Twelve ounces? Does the rule apply to Brooke Shields as well as Lee Haney?

Here's a good rule of thumb. Take your body weight in pounds. Divide the figure in half. That's your daily intake in ounces. A two-hundred-pounder should drink a hundred ounces a day of pure water. Not juice, coffee, tea, or soda—these are digested as foods and don't serve the purpose water does.

Start customizing your diet today. Take advantage of all the top-quality protein sources you have available, not to mention some top-notch protein supplements. You may have to spend some time finding your optimum diet, but any bodybuilder knows that the easy things are seldom worth pursuing.

Tom Platz works on the T-bar rowing for his back.

15
ROUTINES

Bodybuilders are fascinated by routines. Many believe that the routine holds the secret to success. Whereas some star bodybuilders guard their routines, refusing to give them out to writers of the muscle press, most in fact will list their exercises freely, giving details of sets and reps, and poundages.

First off let's admit that champion bodybuilders too frequently settle into a rigid routine once they have found out what works for their individual body makeup. But minor changes are always being made. A few bodybuilders change around their training programs completely, but these are in the minority.

There is no *secret* routine that works for everybody. There are too many other variables. Frequency is important. Intensity factors, too, have to be related to your level of experience and your innate ability to tolerate strenuous physical exercise. Nutrition is another field of tremendous importance to the success of a bodybuilder.

So the routines presented in this chapter are only suggestions. Don't feel that you have to follow them exactly. By the same token don't add more exercises, thinking that the more exercises one does the better the progress. The common mistake in bodybuilding is overwork. Many fall into this trap. They start with a good basic exercise, like the way it feels, and include it in their routine. Next someone shows them a new chest movement, then they read about a special shoulder-widening lift, a new abdominal exercise, and pretty soon their workout is twice its original length, a definite chore to complete.

Typically, muscle enthusiasts will add exercises to their routines but be loath to drop any for fear of missing out on the benefits of a particular movement. This is the mistake: long-drawn-out routines are not the way to build muscle. Your aim should be to pulverize a muscle in as short a time as possible, then stop and go on to the next area. There are a zillion routines, but here are a few that have proved useful over the years.

THE HARD-GAINER'S ROUTINE

Have a difficult time putting on muscle size? Hard gainers are frequently small-boned and have a limited allocation of muscle cells. Not all small-boned people, however, have a low number of muscle cells.

Frequently a genetic superior can get away with eating junk food. A hard gainer cannot. A gifted bodybuilder can train haphazardly and irregularly—hard gainers cannot.

If you are a hard gainer, buckle down to a strict training regime. Do not miss workouts, eat well, rest intelligently. In other words, you cannot afford to stray from the straight and narrow path necessary for bodybuilding success.

Aaron Baker shows perfect form on the dumbbell lateral raise exercise.

HARD-GAINER'S ROUTINE

Chest	Sets	Reps
Medium-grip bench press (elbows back)	5 ×	6
Bent-arm flyes	3 ×	12

Legs

Back squat (feet on block)	4 ×	8
Leg press (45 degrees)	3 ×	12

Shoulders

Press behind neck (from racks)	4 ×	6
Lateral raise (45 degrees, facing incline bench)	3 ×	10

Back

Medium-grip chin (elbows back)	5 ×	10
T-bar rows	3 ×	10

Biceps

Standing dumbbell curl	4 ×	8
Incline dumbbell curl (35 degrees)	3 ×	10

Triceps

Lying triceps stretch	4 ×	8
Close-grip bench press (elbows in)	3 ×	10

Abdominals

Crunches	3 ×	15

HEAVY AND LIGHT ROUTINE

This type of training regime is becoming more and more popular today, since modern experts agree there is evidence that training both heavy and light stimulates different growth areas of the muscles.

Often heavy training translates into multi-joint movements such as bench presses, dips, and squats. Light training is frequently the use of isolation exercises such as thigh extensions and concentration curls.

The important point to bear in mind is not to confuse light reps with fast reps where the speed exceeds a certain rate and momentum takes over (and takes away from the usefulness of the exercise). Keep your reps under control . . . make the muscle work!

There are two ways to use the heavy and light system.

1. You can perform several sets of an exercise with heavy weights (and low reps) and then perform some lighter sets (with high reps) using the same exercise.
2. You can perform a basic (multijoint) exercise using heavy weights, and then, after several heavy sets, you can change to an isolation (lighter exercise) and use high reps for three or four sets.

HEAVY AND LIGHT ROUTINE # 1

(Same exercises)	Sets	Reps
Shoulders		
Press behind neck	4	5
	3	12
Thighs		
Squat	5	4
	3	15
Chest		
Bench press	5	5
	4	12
Back		
T-bar row	4	4
	4	15
Biceps		
Barbell curl	4	5
	3	15
Triceps		
Close-grip bench press	4	5
Calves		
Calf raise (standing)	4	8
	3	25
Abdominals		
Roman chair situp	3	10
	3	50

Cybex lateral raises as demonstrated by California's Brad Verrett.

HEAVY AND LIGHT ROUTINE #2

Shoulders

Press behind neck	5	5-6
Incline lateral raise (with face toward bench)	3	12

Thighs

Squat	5	4
Hack slide	4	12

Chest

Bench press	5	4
Incline flye	4	15

Back

T-bar row	5	5
Lat-machine pulldown (wide grip)	4	15

Biceps

Barbell curl	5	5-6
High bench flat curl	4	15

Triceps

Close-grip bench press	4	4
Lat machine pressdown	4	12

Abdominals

Roman chair situp	4	10
Crunch	3	25

Calves

Seated calf raise	4	10
Donkey calf raise	4	25

EXECUTIVE'S ROUTINE

Office work can be stressful. It can also make you flabby. Weight-training exercises can help keep you both firm and fit. You want a steel-worker's body while working at a desk job? Good for you. According to statistics, if you are fit and strong you'll do better in the boardroom, too. The sought-after image by corporate directors, executives, and managers is that of a strong, virile body with an equally tough personality.

You may not have the time or inclination to build a Mr. Olympia–type physique, but the following routine will give you a body of steel, or something of the kind.

EXECUTIVE'S ROUTINE

Warm-up	Sets	Reps
Stationary bike	(6–12 minutes)	

Chest

	Sets	Reps
Medium-grip bench press	3	15

Thighs

	Sets	Reps
Hack lift (hold barbell behind legs, with heels on block)	2	12–15

Calves

	Sets	Reps
Standing calf raise (barbell across shoulders)	2	15

Shoulders

	Sets	Reps
Alternate seated dumbbell press	2	15

Back

	Sets	Reps
Bent-over row (barbell to waist)	2	15

Biceps

	Sets	Reps
Barbell curl	2	15

Triceps

	Sets	Reps
Barbell triceps stretch	2	12

Abdominals

	Sets	Reps
Seated knee raise	1	50
Broomstick twist	1	200

Cardiovascular

Rope jumping	(2 sets of 3 to 4 minutes each)	

Incline laterals performed by Rich Gaspari.

ONE-EXERCISE-PER-BODY-PART ROUTINE

Save time with this one. You should train hard on each movement and limit your rest time between sets. It is important when using just-one-exercise-per-body-part to make sure that the exercises selected are the best there are. In the following routine, the movements have been chosen that best work the belly of the muscle rather than just the upper or lower sections.

ONE-EXERCISE-PER-BODY-PART ROUTINE

Chest	Sets	Reps
Medium-grip bench press	6	9
Shoulders		
Seated dumbbell press (elbows out)	6	8
Thighs		
Parallel squat (heels on blocks)	6	6–10
Calves		
Donkey calf raise (feet parallel)	6	15–20
Back		
Wide-grip chin behind neck	6	10
Biceps		
Incline dumbbell curl	6	8
Triceps		
Close-grip parallel-bar dip	6	10
Abdominals		
Hanging knee raise	4	15–20

ASPIRING CHAMPS INTERMEDIATE ROUTINE

If you are really serious about your bodybuilding, you do have to put in plenty of sets and reps. You have to hit the muscles from different angles. The following off-season routine should be performed twice a week, but never all at one time. It should be split into two or three sections. Be businesslike about its execution. Make the muscles do the work. Concentrate on stressing the muscle when you train. Do not merely endeavor to *lift* the weight.

INTERMEDIATE ROUTINE

Chest	Sets	Reps
Bench press	5	6–8
Incline bench press	4	8
Flat bench flye	4	10
Thighs		
Squat (heels raised)	5	6–10
Leg press (45 degrees)	4	10–12
Thigh curl	4	12
Calves		
Standing calf raise (machine)	4	15–20
Seated calf raise (machine)	4	15–20
Shoulders		
Seated press behind neck	5	6–8
Lateral dumbbell raise	4	10
Bent-over lateral raise	4	12–15
Back		
Wide-grip chin behind neck	4	10
Lat pulley (palms parallel to chest)	4	10–12
T-bar row	4	10
Biceps		
Barbell curl	4	6
Incline dumbbell curl	4	8
Preacher bench curl (90 degrees)	4	10
Triceps		
Close-grip bench press	4	6–8
Lying triceps stretch	4	10
Pulley pushdown on lat machine	4	12

Abdominals

Roman chair situp	3	25
Hanging leg raise	3	15

Forearms

Reverse curl	4	12–15
Wrist curl	4	12

Don Ross of Gold's Gym, California, performs hack slides.

PRE-CONTEST ROUTINE

You should begin a pre-contest routine ten to fourteen weeks before competing. It's best to make the switch over a week or two before you start your dieting so you are not overwhelmed by having to change your calorie intake and your training routine at the same time.

A pre-contest routine should include plenty of isolation exercises, movements that separate the muscles and "pop" them out when they are posed. Dumbbells and cables are used more frequently at this stage than during an off-season training period.

As you get into the pre-contest routine, it is a good idea to change over from working each body part twice weekly to three times weekly.

Finally, you may experience some discomfort with energy levels and recuperation. If this is severe, take a day or two off and then resume training. It is important that you try to maintain good intensity during your workout. This will serve to keep muscle mass at a time when your limited calorie intake will be encouraging muscle atrophy.

PRE-CONTEST ROUTINE

Chest		Sets	Reps
Bench press to neck		5	8–10
Incline dumbbell bench press		5	8–10
Flat bench flye	} superset	4	10
Cable crossover		4	10

Shoulders		Sets	Reps
Seated dumbbell press	} superset	5	8
Seated dumbbell lateral raise		4	10
Bent-over lateral raise		4	12
Alternate forward dumbbell raise		4	12

Thighs			
Hack lift (knees out)		5	10
Thigh extension		5	10–15
Lunges		4	12
Thigh curl		5	10–12

Calves			
Standing calf raise		4	15–20
Seated calf raise		4	15
Donkey calf raise		4	15–25

Back			
Wide-grip cable pulldown to front		4	10
Pulldown to chest		4	12
Single-arm dumbbell row		4	10
Seated cable row		4	12
Prone hyperextension		4	10–15

Biceps			
Incline dumbbell curl		4	10
Preacher bench dumbbell curl (90 degrees)		4	8–10
Lying dumbbell curl		4	10
Seated concentration curl		4	12

Triceps			
Seated dumbbell triceps stretch		4	10
Cradle bench pulley (facedown)		4	10
Triceps pressdowns		4	10–12
Bent-over dumbbell kickback		4	8–10

Abdominals			
Broomstick twist		3	200
Hanging knee raise	} superset	3	20
Crunch		3	20
Lying half situp		3	15

Forearms			
Reverse curl	} superset	5	10–12
Wrist curl		5	10

Brad Verrett performs the press behind neck.

Ali Mala works his rear delts in the bent-over dumbbell flye movement.

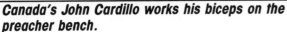

Canada's John Cardillo works his biceps on the preacher bench.

MUSCLE-SIZE-BUILDING ROUTINE

Basic multijoint exercises should form the core of any size-increasing routine. They work the large muscle mass areas. It might be a good idea to pyramid the weights when working on this type of program. That is to say, add weight for each set while decreasing the reps. This serves to thoroughly warm up the muscle for each movement.

As with most long routines, this program will work best if you split it into two parts, performing the first part on Mondays and Thursdays and the second part on Tuesdays and Fridays.

Most bodybuilders use a mass-building routine two or three times a year for six to ten weeks at a time.

MASS-BUILDING ROUTINE

Monday and Thursday	Sets	Reps
Abdominals		
Roman chair situp	3	20–30
Thighs		
Back squats	6	10/8/6/4/3/2
Back		
Deadlift	4	6/4/3/3
T-bar row	6	10/8/6/4/3/2
Trapezius		
Shrug (barbell in front)	4	10/8/6/4
Biceps		
Barbell curl	4	10/8/6/4
Calves		
Seated calf raise	4	15/10/10/8
Tuesday and Friday		
Back		
Prone hyperextensions	2	15–20
Chest		
Bench press	6	10/8/6/4/2/2
Incline bench press	4	10/8/6/4
Shoulders		
Press behind neck	4	8/6/4/3
Upright row	4	8/6/4/3
Triceps		
Lying triceps extension	4	10/8/6/6

Seated dumbbell curls form a part of John Hnatyschak's arm-training routine.

16

VASCULARITY

The Good, the Bad, and the Ugly

There are many qualities that a bodybuilder must possess if he or she is to be successful in physique competition: muscle size, shape, and separation; muscular definition, hardness, density and thickness, symmetry, balance and proportions; good skin and color plus an aesthetic quality to the physique. There is one other quality I didn't mention that can enhance your physique (but not necessarily), especially under poor, flat lighting. It is *vascularity*.

Before I go any further, perhaps we should define what vascularity is. Many people probably have their own definition, but I don't think I'm too far from the mark by saying that vascularity is that state of being when the veins of the body are enlarged and highly visible on the surface of the skin. To some, huge veins crisscrossing the body is their idea of physical perfection. To others, veins are ugly, something to be avoided. It comes down to a matter of personal preferences and tastes. Personally (and this is just *my* subjective opinion), while I admit that veins do attract attention to the physique and definitely add a rugged look to the body, they are not the be-all or end-all for a competitive bodybuilder.

To me, of all the qualities I have just mentioned, vascularity is the least important. Why? Because you can possess all of the other more important qualities — size, shape, separation, density, definition, symmetry, etc — but not be excessively vascular and do quite well in contests. Larry Scott, Bill Pearl, Arnold Schwarzenegger, and Frank Zane were not especially vascular and still won Mr. Olympia and Mr. Universe titles. Or you can be very vascular but not possess many of the other qualities and miss placing every time. For example, some people are genetically disposed to having veins closer to the surface of their skin and to being very vascular without being defined or muscular. Vascularity alone will never win you a contest if you lack the other qualities.

So why care about vascularity at all? Who needs it? If you are a competitive bodybuilder, you do, that's who! As former Pro Mr. America (and one of the most vascular bodybuilders ever) Don Ross said on the topic: "Vascularity is like the frosting on the cake. Without muscular definition it looks ridiculous, but on a cut physique veins are as natural as wide shoulders on a

John Hnatyschak.

swimmer or big calves on a football lineman. Vascularity is the final finishing touch to your physique. Veins can be an edge, that little something extra that can mean the difference between winning and losing."

Actually, if you are in good shape, cut and hard and defined, and if you've carbed up properly and pumped up right, it will be impossible not to show some degree of vascularity. The purpose of this chapter is to show you things that will increase your vascularity and things to avoid which will lessen it.

Before I get into all of that, I should reiterate that while veins can be good, they can also be bad. *MuscleMag International* editor and world-famous bodybuilding author Greg Zulak points this out: "Veins that are long and full and running in line with the shape and contour of a muscle, like

the huge cephalic vein Arnold Schwarzenegger had running down his biceps, enhance the look of the muscle. But little snakelike veins criss-crossing all over the arms, delts, pecs, and thighs, veins that run contrary to the natural line and shape of a particular muscle, can be distracting from your appearance and decrease your aesthetic appeal."

One of the benefits of vascularity, aside from any appearance-enhancing look to your physique, is the building of the vascular system itself. Bigger veins means more blood flow to the muscles, so more nutrients can feed the muscles. Also, more lactic acid and waste products can be removed after muscular exertion: bigger veins means more stamina.

While vascularity is partly an inherited trait, it mostly results from a specific style of training.

Michael Ashley and Shane Dimora.

Vascularity training involves high reps, high sets, intense quality training (little rest between sets), and lots and lots of pumping. People who do lots of supersets are often very vascular. Norman Zale, frequent contributor to *MuscleMag International*, recommends really gripping the bar hard and doing slow, concentrated reps with high intensity to increase vascularity.

Clint Beyerle, in my opinion the most vascular bodybuilder of all time and a perennial contender for the Mr. America title back in the late 1970s, did from twenty-four to thirty-five sets per body part and rested only thirty seconds between sets. Don Ross, as mentioned earlier, was also extremely vascular, but it wasn't always so. Ross found his vascularity radically increased when he followed a training routine that included eight to twelve tri-sets per body part. As his mus-

cles blew up, so did the size and number of his veins. Later on, Ross devised a style of training he called "step bombing," which involved decreasing the weight each set while resting only ten seconds between sets. This allowed him to keep his reps up and train with ferocious intensity, and keep building more vascularity.

Canadian bodybuilder Mike Watson, who won the Mr. Canada title numerous times, was vascular to the nth degree. His veins were like fire hoses! Like Ross and Beyerle, Watson believed in high sets, high-intensity, and lots of supersets for each muscle group. Mike believed you had to really blowtorch a muscle to bring out the vascularity.

So training like a powerlifter, that is, doing heavy sets, low reps, and resting long periods between sets, is out, as far as vascularity is con-

The amazing Rick Valente.

Author Don Ross practices what he preaches.

cerned. Nor is heavy-duty-style training the thing to do if you are after vascularity. This is very intense but is too short in duration to cause much pump or to bring out vascularity unless you are genetically gifted that way. If you look at old pictures of heavy-duty advocate Mike Mentzer when he was in his prime, while he was huge, thick, and dense, he showed little vascularity. Personally, I think had Mike added some vascularity-style training to this bodybuilding regimen (in conjunction with his heavy-duty workouts), he would have added more detail to his physique, built more capillary size, become more vascular, and looked even more impressive.

There are many other factors when it comes to increasing vascularity. Some of these are lowering body-fat levels (lower body fat means thinner skin, so the veins are more visible), enlarging blood vessels, increasing blood pressure, raising glycogen levels, and greatly increasing blood flow to the muscles, forcing the veins and capillaries to enlarge to accommodate the increased blood volume. I'll get to these factors shortly.

Let's first look at some other reasons for increasing or decreasing vascularity. For example, take smoking. Smoking decreases vascularity by constricting blood vessels. Bodybuilders who smoke — and fortunately most North American bodybuilders don't, although many European ones do as an appetite suppressant — will find their vascularity waning unless counteracted by other drugs (but that's another story).

The B-vitamin niacin, a natural vasodilator of blood vessels, can increase your vascularity temporarily. Mr. Universe Johnny Fuller was one bodybuilder who claimed that taking a niacin tablet before a workout helped bring out vascularity. Many people use niacin just before going on stage to pose at a contest. Niacin causes a flushing action in which the skin appears to glow as it is infused with blood, and the veins become more prominent. This is especially true in the face, neck, chest, shoulders, and arms.

All this sounds great, but using niacin has two drawbacks. Taking it isn't an altogether pleasant experience, as your skin will burn and tingle and your scalp will itch and "crawl" as the flush comes on. But it's only temporary and

Upright rows done the Shawn Ray way.

passes shortly, usually in about twenty minutes. Second, taking niacin causes you to have red, blotchy areas all over your body, especially on your upper body. This can give an appearance from mildly distracting to terribly unsightly. The lighter the person's skin, usually the worse they look. Blacks who have very dark skin can usually get away with taking niacin without showing any blotchiness, but they seem to be the only ones.

If you decide to take niacin (I recommend 200 to 400 mg) at a show, try to time it about twenty minutes before you go on stage to pose. Take it too soon and the flush will be over before you go on stage; take it too late and it won't come on until your posing routine is over, rendering the effect useless. I recommend you experiment with niacin so you see how you react to it. Then you can make an educated decision as to whether you want to use it at a contest. Be aware—niacin does not suit everyone.

Another thing that can constrict blood vessels and curtail vascularity is cold. Ever try to pump up when you are freezing? You can't pump properly, and the veins go into hiding. But on the other hand, heat seems to bring out vascularity. Ever notice how after lying out in the hot sun your veins stand out? Well, you can use this knowledge to your advantage at your next show. The rule is, if you're trying to increase your vascularity, keep warm.

As I write this I just got back from Washington, D.C., where I watched Hannu Selin (husband of Margo) compete in a bodybuilding show. On the way to the show Hannu wore three sweatsuits, though it was in the 90s. He also turned on the car heater! So it was about 120 degrees in the car. Backstage, when the other contestants were pumping up in their posing trunks, Hannu pumped up in his three pairs of sweats. Needless to say, he was hotter than hell and sweating like someone in a sauna. But when it came time to go on stage, Hannu peeled off his sweatsuits to reveal a ripped physique with veins like water hoses all over his body. Other contestants were actually talking to their bodies in frustration, saying, "Come on! You [veins] were there yesterday when I was tanning. Where did you go?" So remember, keep warm, your veins

Amazing is the only word for this most muscular by Californian Mike Christian.

will love you for it.

Another technique to increase vascularity is to practice holding various poses for long periods of time, say fifteen to thirty seconds or even longer. Don Ross used this method. He recommends that you hit a pose, hold your breath, and flex with all your might. Try to force the breath out, but don't actually release it. This causes blood pressure to rise. Your face will flush and veins will pop up everywhere. But be careful when trying this. If you push too hard you can break blood vessels in your face and eyes, so go easy at first. Build up slowly to this technique. Start by holding poses for five seconds, then ten, and keep adding time. Also, if you have high blood pressure or any medical problems, check with your doctor first.

Even your attitude and self-confidence levels can determine how vascular you can get. I've noticed that people who are cocky, sure of themselves, and full of confidence at a show, like Rich Gaspari, are extremely vascular. It seems that if you are arrogant enough to be "puffed up with ego" and "full of yourself," if you will, your veins

will pop out more. But people who are nervous, frightened, and lacking confidence will be less vascular than they normally would. This is because fear constricts the blood vessels, too. Of course, the only way to be confident and cocky is to make sure you are in your best shape come contest time. You can't fake confidence.

Carbohydrate loading is one of the best ways to greatly increase vascularity on the day of your show. If you have low levels of glycogen in the muscles, your muscles will look drained, flat, and smaller, and the veins will be much smaller and noticeable too. Carb loading is based on the principles of glycogen super compensation. That is, by depleting your muscles of all glycogen stores and then suddenly eating a lot of carbohydrates, the body overcompensates and stores more glycogen in the muscles than is normally possible. If done properly, carb loading results in fuller, harder-looking muscles and vastly improved vascularity. Fresh fruit, brown rice, and baked potatoes are favorites for carb loading. Trainer Gun Sikk recommends eating a combination of simple and complex carbs to get differ-

John Hnatyschak.

ent rates of release. For example, you might eat some cantaloupe, raisins, pears, apples, then some rice and potatoes, etc. Gun has found it best to carb deplete slowly but to carb up fairly fast.

But be careful. This technique does take some experimentation to find out how much time you need to deplete and how much time and how much you can eat to load up with. Timing is essential, and if carb loading is mistimed or overdone, it can result in water retention and a smooth, bloated look. Try experimenting in the off-season before trying it at an actual contest.

Daniel Duchaine once wrote that those who had low blood pressure, specifically a low diastolic number (below 90), would have trouble making their veins show. Duchaine felt the low blood pressure was often caused by anemia and was common among weight-trained athletes (especially women) due to overtraining and severe contest dieting. Anemia (the reduction of red blood cells) will result in a lowering of blood pressure. Duchaine thinks that some anabolic steroids like Anatrophin (almost impossible to get now) and Anadrol-50 will build up the red-blood-cell count very fast. He recommends one 50-mg Anadrol-50 tab a day the last ten days before a show to rebuild the red-blood-cell count and allow you to better endure the stresses of carb depletion and contest preparation.

According to Duchaine, Anatrophin and Anadrol-50 were created to combat anemia. He thinks that the drawn, flat, overtrained look you so often see at contests is due as much to a lowering of red blood cells and blood volume as it is to a lack of glycogen in the muscles. Anemic people just can't carb deplete and load up properly.

For natural bodybuilders, B-12 shots will help if you are slightly anemic. As well, certain foods help to prevent anemia. Gun Sikk recommends red meat twice a week when dieting for a contest, as well as high-grain liver tabs daily. Also, Sikk has found that some free-form aminos help as well.

Many high-androgen anabolic steroids such as Dianabol, DMU, Anadrol-50, Equipoise, Parabolan and Finaject cause an increase in vascu-

larity. I'm not recommending these to you, but you won't get that severe vascularity you see on many top pros naturally. No doubt about it, drugs play a major role in these extreme cases of vascularity. But with drug testing gaining popularity, use of these drugs may not be possible.

Some other drugs help to increase vascularity. L-Dopa is one of them. Duchaine wrote in one of the *Underground Steroid* updates about the use of the drug Catapres for greatly increased vascularity, due to an increase in blood pressure. I know that a lot of people knock guys like Duchaine and Jeff Feliciano, calling them pseudo-experts and claiming they are not qualified to give advice, but I have observed that many times what they have to say, while not backed by medical experts, turns out to be valid in the real world. For example, they were right about Nolvadex preventing aromatization.

Back to Catapres. It is an antihypertension medicine used to control high blood pressure. You may wonder why you would use a medicine to reduce high blood pressure when I just said that low blood pressure reduces vascularity. If you take Catapres it will reduce your blood pressure, but upon stopping use of it, a rebound ef-

fect is experienced and your blood pressure will go up much higher than normal (temporarily) and result in increased vascularity. Duchaine recommends one Catapres tablet a day for twelve days and then stopping four days before your contest. On the day of the show, the rebound effect should be occurring (hopefully) resulting in much greater vascularity than normally possible. Again, if you are considering the use of Catapres (or any drug) *consult your physician.*

Anything that reduces body fat will improve vascularity, so strict dieting is essential. As well, vascularity, as mentioned, has a lot to do with cardiovascular efficiency. Volume training of the kind I recommended before (high sets, high reps, little rest time) increases heart rate and respiration. That's why running, cycling, stationary biking, and other forms of aerobics can increase vascularity.

So there you have it. The ins and outs and whys and hows of vascularity. Keep some of these things in mind before your next contest, and you too can walk on stage like a human anatomy chart. As Don Ross once said, "The aesthetic purists will think you're disgusting, but the hard-core bodybuilding fans will love you."

Look at those amazing arms of fifty-year-old Larry Scott.

17

AGING

Getting Older and Better

Not too many youngsters worry about aging — it's natural not to think too much about the distant future. And besides, if you have a healthy, optimistic ego, you probably think you won't ever get old. Well, here's the truth: *You will either die early or you will get old.* Neither is a particularly pleasant thought, is it? So let's accept the inevitability of aging.

Whatever age you are now, you should make the needed changes to prepare for your older years. Age itself does not automatically preclude your being both strong and well built; healthy, fit, and virile. There are thousands of people of both sexes who are in their seventies and eighties, and are in better physical condition today than they were in their forties. Not only that, but because they have chosen to follow a proper exercise and diet program, many of them look more vital and healthy than they did in their younger years.

Let's admit right from the start that we cannot totally defeat age. However well preserved we are, however strong, fit, healthy, irrespective of feeling full of pep and energy or whether or not we can keep wrinkles and fat levels down to a minimum . . . there will be certain things about us that will give away our approximate age. Some people even resort to regular face lifts (they need to be regular because they drop every year or two), tummy tucks, and fat vacuuming . . . but there's always an age giveaway somewhere. So, realistically, the best we can hope for is comments like, "Wow, do you ever look good for your age!" Or, "Hey, you must be thirty years older than me, but you look fantastic!" Only seldom will you get a resounding: "I didn't know you were sixty-five, you look like you're only in your forties!" Well, you may get the comment regularly, but invariably the individual will be knowingly stretching the truth somewhat. Think about it. You probably know people who are well preserved, who are fit, youthful, and strong for their age, but you know *really* that they are no spring chickens.

Don't let me get you down. You can look good as you get older. There are strange compensations that come with added years. Here's what Vince Gironda told me: "As you get older, I find that it is easier to keep fat levels down. The muscles have better delineation." Another

Seated cable rowing by Larry Scott.

Sixty-year-old Reg Park working on the leg-press machine.

aid to the older bodybuilder is that you will know your body intimately. Older people can make changes almost from day to day. In his sixties and seventies, for example, John Grimek could, at will, alter his body weight up or down by ten pounds within only a few days. "From experience you have better control," he says.

The following are my suggestions for holding on to your vitality, strength, energy, and physique right into your autumn years.

WEIGHT TRAINING

Plan slow, gradual increases in exercise intensity, duration, and frequency. Train each body part on a split routine, twice per week. Split your routine into three parts and train a third of your workout on day one, the next third on day two, and the final third on day three. Day four is a rest day. On day five train the first third again, day six is the second third, day seven is the final third. Rest on day eight. This is known as the three-days-on, one-day-off routine. As an alternative to this, you might split your workout in two and perform half your routine on day one and the other half on day two. Day three would be a rest day, and day four would be the first half again . . . and so on. This is an ideal routine for those who like to keep the weekend free. You can train on Mondays and Tuesdays, and on Thursdays and Fridays.

The older you get, the more attention you must pay to warming up before attempting strenuous poundages. Exercise style should never be sloppy. Definitely no bouncing, hoisting, bridging, tossing, or uncontrolled swinging. Keep control of the resistance at all times.

It is a good idea to perform all your triceps movements in one workout (presses, bench presses, dips, triceps stretches). All your movements involving the biceps should be kept together too (curls, chins, pulldowns, rowing). This is known as the push-pull method and allows the joint action involved to get sufficient rest between workouts. The wear and tear on the joints is halved. In similar vein, keep strenuous exercise involving the knee joint to twice-weekly workouts. Many bodybuilders, for example, train their chests and shoulders on separate days. This would subject the joints to excess wear and tear.

After a layoff always return to your training very slowly. Start with one extremely light set of each exercise. Gradually increase the poundages and sets each workout. Soon you will be back in the groove.

NUTRITION

Older people should eat smaller amounts of meat, always lean (cut the fat off) or try to stay with fish or poultry.

Much of your food should consist of fresh fruit, whole grains, and vegetables. Sugar (including raw sugar) and honey should be kept at under thirty-five pounds per year. (The average, U.S. consumption is 100 pounds per year.) Avoid soft drinks and high-sugar foods by checking the labels on all items. Never overload the stomach at any one meal.

STRESS

Work only at a job you enjoy. Most U.S. and Canadian centenarians work for themselves, and the most common single reason given for reaching advanced old age was that they never worried about anything.

Try to keep your family intact. Divorces and separation from children or loved ones are not conducive to achieving healthy old age. Avoid stress if possible.

SUPPLEMENTATION

Take a daily multivitamin mineral one-a-day pill. Supplement with additional vitamin C to bolster the immune system, and vitamin E to enable blood cells to carry more oxygen. Further supplementation such as iron or calcium may be recommended by your doctor.

SMOKING

Don't do it! If right now you are caught up in the tobacco habit, do whatever is necessary to stop. That first month without nicotine can be hell, but after that period you will be so against cigarettes that you will hardly be able to believe you were once a smoker. You will probably not crave cigarettes again. I don't want to list the horrendous things associated with smoking, since enough publicity has been produced of late to put smokers into a state of shock. Sufficient to say that cigarette smoking is one of the most damaging things you can do to your vital organs. Stop today.

STRETCHING

I know. Real men don't eat quiche. And real bodybuilders don't stretch. Well, times they are a-changin'. As you get older, you *need* to stretch. It's important that muscles, tendons, and ligaments be kept long and limber. It's good to have the fullest mobility in your joints.

Begin every workout with five or ten minutes of various stretches. You can change them around or try new positions all the time. Start by sitting on the floor and stretching out to touch your toes. Then move your feet out to your side and feel the pull in your legs and hamstrings. . . . Be inventive. Hold each stretch for five to ten seconds. Then release slowly. Do not bounce or move ballistically. All stretches must be done slowly and with caution.

AEROBIC EXERCISE

Your weight-training exercises can be made aerobic by using lighter weights, more reps, and less rest between sets; but the drawback is that you probably won't be holding on to as much mass if you train in this way.

Personally, I would keep my aerobic activity separate from bodybuilding workouts. Take three to five aerobic breaks lasting from twenty to forty minutes by going for a long powerwalk (arms swinging high, legs striding out), jog, cycle, row, swim, or hike. Or you may prefer assorted aerobics to music, dancing, jumping, arm waving, twisting. . . . The basic idea behind aerobic programs is to promote fitness (cardiovascular) and fat loss. You should aim to elevate your heart rate and keep it elevated for the duration of the routine. It should not exceed 80 percent of your maximum heart rate. Subtract your age from 220 to estimate your maximum heart rate. For example, a person who is fifty years old has a maximum heart rate of 170 (220 minus 50). Eighty percent of 170 is 136. This person should try to exercise to a point where his or her heart rate is elevated but does not exceed 136.

Perennial Irvin "Zabo" Kozewski works on the lat pulldown exercise.

DRINK WATER

Water, water everywhere but not a drop to drink. Scientists tell us that we are composed of about 70 percent water. They also tell us that we need eight to ten glasses a day to keep in optimum health. What we are seldom told is that a heck of a lot of this planet's fresh water is undrinkable. Heavy industry, especially around big cities and the Great Lakes area of Canada and the U.S.A., has polluted enormous underground oceans of water. Tapwater is treated with chlorine and other chemicals to "cleanse" it for human consumption . . . but still there are daily reports from all over the country about unsafe water supplies. Right now supermarkets, restaurants, and drinking establishments are selling, in record amounts, specially bottled water shipped in from France, Sweden, and Italy. What a catastrophe. North America, the land of a zillion lakes, streams, and rivers, has become the world's biggest importer of bottled drinking water. True, some of this consumption is motivated by the excitement of tasting pure French mineral water from "La Source," but an ever-increasing amount is consumed from outright fear of drinking from our own potentially unreliable water reservoirs. Water, fresh pure water, is essential to optimum health. We must seek it out and consume six to ten glasses per day.

THINK POSITIVE

Negative thinking is linked to poor health. Many psychologists believe that what we think, whether written, spoken, or merely remaining in our minds, determines our behavior, health, and well-being. If we allow ourselves to sing the blues for too long, we are inviting health problems. In one study involving several dozen people aged sixty to ninety, those with negative thought patterns, who were pessimistic in outlook, tended to have lower levels of certain immune-system cells than those of a more optimistic frame of mind.

Try not to allow negativism to rule your outlook. Life is yours for the making. That's why you're reading this book. You believe that you can control your own success. It's not reality itself that produces frailty and poor health, but the way we handle and consider that reality.

Frank Richards of England.

18

JUDGING

Placing Contestants

Ricky Wayne says he's never known an audience that didn't judge a physique contest correctly. Rory Leidelmeyer says, "You can't fool an audience; they know. If the judges choose the wrong man, the audience will let them know. For the most part, audiences are composed of hard-core bodybuilders who know bodybuilding."

Going on the above views, Bertil Fox, Tom Platz, Mike Mentzer, and Ed Corney should all have been Mr. Olympia winners. . . . I'm not saying the audience is always wrong, but I am utterly convinced that they are not always right! They tend to be overinfluenced by sheer size, mesmerized by most-muscular poses, and oblivious to those faults of bodybuilders who have a single, glaringly-obvious-to-the-judges weak point, such as poor abdominals, high calves, nonexistent necks, or totally underdeveloped lower backs. . . .

As Publisher of *MuscleMag International,* I have sat in the front rows of more major contests than probably anyone else. For starters I have been to twenty-five of the Nabba Annual Mr. Universe contests in London, and have seen stars like Jack Delinger, Bill Pearl, Clancy Ross, Reg Park, Dennis Tinerino, Tom Sansone, Chet Yorton, Sergio Oliva, Serge Nubret, Lou Ferrigno, Ken Waller, Franco Columbu, Boyer Coe, Chris Dickerson, Arnold Schwarzenegger, Frank Zane, Bertil Fox compete with the Nabba organization. I have witnessed most WBBG Mr. Worlds, numerous AAU Mr. Americas, and IFBB Mr. Americas, Mr. Worlds, and Mr. Universes. I have attended virtually all the IFBB Professional Grand Prix. I've never missed a professional women's World's Championship, and I've been to every one of Wayne Demilia's Night of Champions events. There are several people in this world who have attended more shows than myself. Oscar Heidenstam, in England, is one. (He has averaged forty-five shows a year for forty years.) Winston Roberts, of Montreal, is possibly another. But I have witnessed more of the top-class international shows than these men, especially from competing organizations. I have attended Wabba Mr. Worlds, AAU Mr. USAs, Nabba Mr. Britains, Teenage Nationals, Mr. International, and a multitude of lesser events. I even attended the Nabba Universe in London *and* the IFBB Mr. Universe and Mr. Olympia held on the same day,

West Germany's superb Anja Langer.

Canada's fastest-rising star, Steve Brisbois.

catching a flight out of London within an hour of the London show's ending and arriving in New York (with the help of the time difference) in time to witness the IFBB Show. Only two others ever did that: Vic Downs and Franklyn Page.

I mention this basically irrelevant waffle to add weight to the fact that since I have seen more top men and women competing than anyone else, I may just know a little about what constitutes a good physique. Currently I do not judge officially. I prefer to use my camera. But I have judged from the local gym contest right up to the Mr. Universe level. And believe me, I could tell you some judging stories that would make your hair curl. But that will have to wait for my bodybuilding exposé book. Judges make one friend per contest and that's it. Give me a camera anytime.

Judging is an art and it is a pretty tough one. The other day I received a letter from a disgruntled reader who complained that judges at top shows should be either competing professional bodybuilders or former professional bodybuilders. His reasoning was that most judges had "never been there," so how could they be good judges? I have to smile at this remark because I have seen the end results of judging by pro bodybuilders. It's well known to Iron Game insiders that pro bodybuilders make terrible judges. Typically they make horrendous mistakes like "forgetting about one of the top competitors" or giving it to so and so "because he had the biggest arms in the show." And not a little racism has been shown by pro bodybuilders over the years. But the best example of incompetence among pro-bodybuilding judges was an otherwise genial former Mr. America who placed his favorite body man first, "because he's a real nice guy!"

No, sir, top bodybuilders for the most part do not make good judges. In the same vein you will find that the best coaches, referees, and trainers were seldom superathletes in their day.

In judging anything one has to use comparison. It was concluded some time ago that the placement system of putting bodybuilders in *order of merit* was superior to the points system where one competitor could be placed well ahead of the field by a couple of overenthusiastic judges.

One of the big problems in judging is how to *weigh the balance* of, say, a person who has a tremendous physique yet whose calf development is very poor, against another competitor who is not so big or defined, yet who has calf development (and everything else) that is in perfect proportion. The same problem occurs over the abnormality of gynecomastia ("bitch tits"). Surely this is a medical condition that conflicts entirely with the aims of bodybuilding as a competitive sport. Yet even today, bodybuilders with advanced cases of bitch tits are given first-place trophies.

The next point to clear up is that some people are born with overlong legs, poor posture, high calves, narrow shoulders, and flat biceps. Should they be forgiven because they are not responsible for their faults? No way. Judge the man, not his unfortunate genetics. Here is where I agree with Rory Leidelmeyer, who says: "To a large degree muscle shape is a genetic quality. Your muscle shape was determined at birth. Be that as it may, misshapen muscles are faults whether the athlete can do anything about them or not. A judge has no right to say, 'That's okay. He was born with that fault.'" The fault, whether it be high calf, or a short biceps, or anything else, must be duly noted and used against the bodybuilder in question.

Judging another person's physique is of course subjective. We only have guidelines to follow. Because the good and bad aspects of body structure have not been isolated to any degree of sophistication, no computer has yet been programmed to judge efficiently. In fact, judges, officials, and bodybuilding authorities regularly disagree, sometimes to a large extent, on what constitutes the *winning physique.* "Remember — the name of the game is bodybuilding," says one judge. "You gotta be big, man! That's the first requirement." "Cuts are what counts," says another. "It doesn't matter how big you are. If you're not cut, size doesn't count for anything!" And then there are the aesthetic critics . . . "Proportion has to be the main consideration. Without it you just don't have a physique worth

Marjo Selin.

Robby Robinson, Gary Strydom, and Bertil Fox pose off at Wayne Demilia's famous Night of Champions.

looking at." Actually, judges tend to favor those types of physiques that most resemble their own. Being basically ectomorphic (skinny), I was never able to attain much muscle size, but I had, and have, reasonable proportion and shape. To this day I favor physiques that are well shaped and proportionate. I know other judges who worship bigness, and invariably they are or were steroid-bloated monsters themselves. Likewise, those who see the superdefined physique as the only way to go invariably are, or were, superdefined themselves.

Personally I would place Bob Paris, Rory Leidelmeyer, Matt Mendenhall, or John Hnatyschak over someone a little sharper, or bigger, but who has a glaring weak point. Frank Zane, at his best, had a super combination of shape, proportion, and cuts. I have yet to see a better-packaged physique. Today's judges, however, see him as outmoded because he doesn't have twenty-inch arms!

Steve Reeves, of course, in his prime was utterly remarkable, although curiously enough his out-of-this-world shape was frequently overlooked when he competed. And he was frequently judged pound for pound like a lump of meat. Bodybuilding history shows that Reeves, in spite of being acclaimed as the world's most perfectly built male (which he was) all too often met with defeat at the hands of bodybuilders like John Grimek and Clarence Ross. Even in 1947, the year he won the Mr. America in Chicago, Reeves was almost beaten by a narrow-shouldered, far-from-dynamic-looking Eric Pedersen. After tying the two men in a deadlock, the judges' ultimate decision was made in favor of Reeves "because his skin was blemish-free." Apparently the Mr. A trophy went to Hercules unchained because poor Eric had a spot of acne.

To be a good judge today you have to be honest and unbiased. But integrity and fairness are useless traits if you do not have competence.

But becoming totally competent takes time and effort. There are so many variables to judging that there are no hard and fast rules. For example, presentation is extremely important. It gains you pluses with the judging panel. But does excellent posing beat a slightly better physique whose posing is poor?

A judge who wishes to excel must look and decide on a physique according to:

MUSCLE MASS

There must be a degree of fullness to the muscles. They must be developed evenly from origin to insertion. Lower forearms, lower triceps, lower biceps, lower thighs should all be fully developed. Those with large bones are at a disadvantage. The muscles do not pop out so dramatically, as is usually the case with men and women with medium-sized bones.

PROPORTION

A pair of 20-inch arms going steady with a set of 14-inch calves is ridiculous. But it happens all the time. The same goes with other muscle groups. What's the use of 29-inch thighs if your arms or calves are only 15 or 16 inches?

Good proportion entails having wide shoulders, narrow hips, balanced thighs, flared lats, stacked pecs . . . with all the smaller muscles built to fit aesthetically with one another.

SYMMETRY

This is a misunderstood term. Symmetry merely means that both sides of the body are equally developed: both thighs, both shoulders, both arms. Actually, most bodybuilders have $1/2$- to 1-inch difference in the size of their arms. It's seldom noticeable. If you are lacking symmetry, train more with dumbbells.

DEFINITION

Yes, definition — the attainment of a low percentage of body fat, especially that fat just beneath the skin — is extremely important. Some critics feel that judges attach too much importance to muscular definition. This, of course, is a matter of opinion. As I write this book, the trend is definitely for judges to give their votes to the most-defined physiques, with the obvious proviso, of course, that the person be pretty well proportioned and well muscled. Years ago many physiques *failed* to win contests because they were considered too muscularly defined. It was considered too "freaky."

It would not be a bad idea for judges to loosen up a little on the body-fat issue because much of the superdefinition of today is achieved by the taking of dangerous prescription drugs that literally burn away excess fat tissue. This puts the athlete at a great risk of overrevving and causing irreversible thyroid-gland problems and even heart trouble. Cut-up drugs are more potentially dangerous than anabolic steroids.

Having said that, it should be added that excellent definition is vital in today's events. The judges can tell instantly if you are ripped or not. First, their eyes go to the abs. If all the layers show up clearly, they know you're in shape. But the next place they look, especially when you do a double biceps pose from the front, is the serratus magnus, that riblike "shark's tooth" muscle under the arms. If it sparkles with crisp delineation, that pretty well says you're ripped. But the last checkpoint for fat is the glutes. Few men and women indeed possess ripped glutes, but if that be the case, you have gone one step further than being ripped. You're *shredded!*

SHAPE

This is a God-given facet to your body. Shape can be improved in everyone, but it's a heck of a lot easier if you have it naturally, like Jon-Jon Park, Bob Paris, Steve Reeves, Scott Wilson, Shawn Ray, Lee Haney, Marjo Selin, Juliette Bergman, Anja Langer, Cory Everson . . . all have excellent natural shape, and they have of course added to it with intelligent training. A person who doesn't possess good shape must definitely work for it. If they do not, then they will never win a physique

contest. Even an individual with great shape must train sensibly. Poor training, especially when combined with heavy drug use, will ruin a naturally shapely physique quicker than you can say anabolic steroid.

Good shape is epitomized by high, wide pecs, barndoor-wide shoulders, a relatively long neck, a small waistline and hips, neat "straight" abs, flaring lats, swelling thighs that have an outer sweep, and plenty of lower quads that tuck into small knees. Swelling, diamond-shaped calves. . . . Not least of all these considerations is perfect posture. Very few top bodybuilders are set up correctly when it comes to body alignment. Bodybuilders with perfect posture who come to mind are John Terilli, Chet Yorton, Jon-Jon Park, Bob Paris, Robby Robinson, Marjo Selin, Cory Everson, and Erika Mes.

Those people with what we traditionally term "good shape" often have those little extras such as straight-across (horizontal) collarbones; small-to-medium-sized wrists, ankles, and knees; a

It's that girl again . . . Cory Everson.

straight lower-pec line; and rows of abdominals that are straight. A few in the game have some areas that are beautifully shaped, yet others that are lacking. No man in this world has more shapely upper arms and shoulders than Mike Christian, yet his calves are a little on the high side. Likewise with Mohamed Makkawy's abs. They are the best in the world, yet nature has endowed him with very poor potential for building impressive thigh biceps. Conversely, Boyer Coe has great arms but poor potential for ab development. Juliette Bergman as yet has no equal in the world when it comes to natural shape, yet she could look utterly perfect if she had a slightly longer neck and better posture.

PRESENTATION

No rules here, but a good posing routine should help you gain an edge. Truthfully, even a magnificent posing presentation will not save you if you are *down* in the judges' assessment.

I'll always remember Charles Gaines's words on posing. His observations always ring true. He tells us things we all know, yet haven't allowed to crystalize in our minds. "Posing is the heart of the thing. Depending on how it is done, you can see in it either everything that is moving and beautiful and dignified about the display of a developed body or everything that is ridiculous and embarrassing about it!" So wrote Gaines in his best-selling tome *Pumping Iron* (Simon and Schuster).

Your posing must move and inspire. There are a zillion ways to do this and too many variables to even suggest *how* you should pose. But you can be sure that great posing will come only to those who study the art . . . and practice the execution. The world's best posers include past champs Ed Corney and Chris Dickerson, plus artists like Russ Testo, John Brown, Cory Everson, Frank Zane, Anja Langer, Mohamed Makkawy, and Tonya Knight.

It is suggested that you study videotapes of the greats and learn the art of posing by imitating some of the moves and innovating on your own. Judges know good posing presentation when they see it. Make sure your routine is neither embarrassing nor ridiculous. Rather it should be in the words of Charles Gaines: "Moving and beautiful and dignified."

The women pose off . . . Bev Francis, Anja Langer, and Marjo Selin.

19

CONTEST DIETING

Ripping Up

Wouldn't it be great to be ripped all the time? Just imagine those bulging defined muscles . . . with you every moment of the day and night.

The truth is of course that very few bodybuilders indeed are ripped all the time. Some men and women hold on to a positive muscular appearance during the off-season, but far too many allow themselves to be overweight during this time. True, you may look impressive in clothes if you are holding a high body weight, but display your physique and you'll impress very few people. Personally I think that an overweight body is given away by a fat face, and I do not think that excess lard on the jowls is conducive to a fit appearance.

To my mind bodybuilders should strive not to be more than ten pounds above their best contest weight during the off-season. This serves a double purpose. 1. They will always look good stripped. 2. The amount of diet and exercise effort to reach that contest-ready condition is minimized.

Competitive bodybuilding is a unique sport in that it requires that a person exhibit maximum muscle mass and minimum body fat at the same time. This in itself is almost an unworkable task. The body *likes* to gain muscle and fat at the same time, and when weight is dropped it's natural to *lose* both at the same time too.

Today cuts are "in." But it wasn't always so. In fact, way back in 1950 a comparatively smooth Steve Reeves beat a harder and more defined Reg Park for the Mr. Universe title in London. At other times John Grimek, Clancy Ross, George Eiferman, and Bill Pearl all beat out more defined physiques to win top titles. In fact, the most defined bodybuilder of the fifties was Vince Gironda, whom many considered too defined, some going as far as to call his thin skin obscene. Another man, Britisher Rueb Martin, got his body fat so low for the Mr. Britain title that the judging panel dismissed him as being "over-defined and muscular" beyond normal. But modern judging panels demand superdefinition and low body-fat levels, so if one wants to place and win in these shows, one has to go along with the style of the day . . . and get ripped. Never before in history has our sport produced title winners

Matt Mendenhall.

Mary Roberts.

with anywhere near the degree of definition that our current champions possess. Today we have women who are more defined than any Mr. Universe or Mr. Olympia from bygone years.

Getting into contest shape is a chore. Few find it easy. Many find it extremely difficult. Some find it impossible. Training is important at this time, but the real fat-burner is diet. And it is diet that bodybuilders traditionally find the most problem. The main mistake is in starting the diet too late. The second-most-common mistake is cutting calories too drastically at the beginning of the diet. This can throw the body into a kind of shock (basal metabolic rate slows down) and actually encourages it to hold on to fat deposits.

So, to start at the beginning, even in the off-season you should be watching your food intake. Keep away from empty-calorie foods that contain high calories but very little real nutrition. When it comes time to diet, cut your food intake gradually. How far out from a contest should you be when you start restricting calories? That depends on how overweight you are. Most begin at about ten to fourteen weeks out, but if you are already in pretty good muscular shape, you may need to diet for only three to five weeks. It is important that even though your diet is restricted in calories, you still maintain adequate nutrition so that your muscle mass shrinks as little as possible. Deciding how little you can eat without interfering with the quality of nutrition takes some common sense. For example, every gram of fat contains nine calories (as opposed to carbohydrate and protein, both of which contain four calories), so it is advisable to keep your fat intake as low as possible. However, eating a diet of zero fat is not advised, nor is it easily accomplished. Some fat is necessary, but make an effort to limit your intake.

Protein is necessary. And a bodybuilder needs more than the one gram for every 2.2 pounds of body weight advocated by the RDA (Recommended Daily Allowance). Most bodybuilding experts agree that we need at least one gram of protein for every pound of body weight.

Carbohydrates, too, are essential, but at this stage of dieting we have to watch our intake. Eat only complex carbohydrates (high-fiber vegeta-bles, fruit, and whole grains as opposed to low-fiber honey, sugar, and juice).

Because we are restricting our food intake, there is a real possibility of not getting all the nutrients our body requires, so . . . it is a good idea to supplement our diets at this time with a high-potency vitamin/mineral tablet and with a top-quality protein powder or amino acid supplement. The latter gives us added protein with no additional calories, so it becomes, theoretically at least, the ideal supplement for the bodybuilder in the throes of contest dieting.

One problem that confronts bodybuilders is just how much fat does one lose. Curiously, it is *not* a matter of "the more the better." Fat is needed in the muscle to keep it round and full. Your job is to eliminate fat from under the skin, so you look ripped on stage. Intramuscular fat should be a welcome boarder. It adds to your size, just like water, which forms 70 percent of your muscle composition. I have seen very ripped bodybuilders who tested out at 10 to 13 percent body fat, yet others, less defined, have registered incredibly low percentages of 3 to 6 percent. If you diet away intramuscular fat or take diuretics to lose water, you run the risk of losing impressive muscle mass and of giving your muscles a flat, stringy appearance.

Having decided to diet down to a ripped condition for a photo session, a contest, or a posing exhibition, you have to plan both your training and your diet. Training itself will not change dramatically. Usually you will need to decrease rest time between sets and perform more isolation exercises (thigh extensions, concentration curls, crossover pulleys) than combination movements (bench pressing, rowing, squatting). Too, you should train each body part two and a half or three times weekly instead of the off-season practice of twice weekly. Finally, use your mind more when exercising. Concentrate on the muscle being worked and squeeze (flex strongly) the muscles while they are being worked. You should not give up using good-sized poundage. Your lower-calorie nutritional intake will take away your fat, but it will also rob you of at least some of your muscle. Keep your weights up as the countdown continues and you will minimize

Frank Richard.

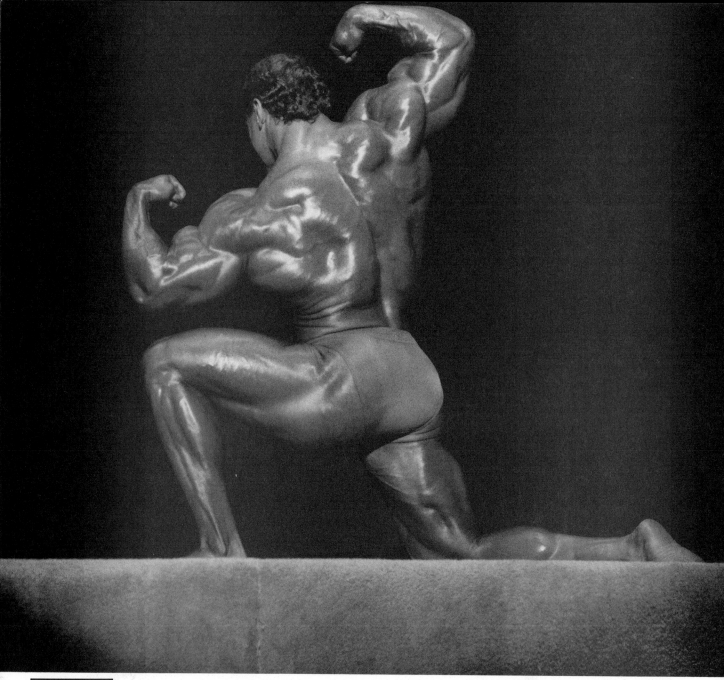

the degree of muscle shrinkage dramatically.

Now for the diet. Let's assume for the sake of argument that you begin your diet eight weeks out from show date. It may be more or less. You need time to lose weight (fat), and there's nothing worse than running out of time as a contest approaches. You end up starving yourself and messing up the whole contest-winning campaign. You could lose your fat too quickly and be left with loose skin and a flat-looking body.

I've said it before but it bears repeating. The point has to be absorbed. *When you begin a diet, begin moderately. Start by gradually reducing your food intake each week or so.* You're in for a shock if you think you can suddenly drop from a 5000-calorie-per-day diet to 1500. You may lose fat by doing this, but you'll lack energy, lose muscle mass, and probably also suffer with severe headaches.

Drop your calories gradually and you will not run out of gas during your workouts, neither will you lose strength or true muscle mass. The general rule of thumb is to start dieting by cutting 200 calories from your total, then dropping a further 100 calories every two or three days. The following pre-contest diet is typical for most successful bodybuilders. I first outlined it in my nutrition book *Rock Hard!* (Warner Books).

Jacques Neuville of France.

Not too many backs as
muscular as this.
Ali Mala shows it all.

Comparing the spreads, Ron Love and Mike Christian.

BREAKFAST

Bran cereal or oats with nonfat milk or soft
  fruit.
Egg whites
Coffee, tea, or water (no sugar, but artificial
  sweetener is acceptable)
Supplements

LUNCH

Broiled fish
One or two green vegetables
Baked potato (no butter or sour cream)
One piece fresh fruit
Coffee, tea, or water (no sugar)

DINNER

Broiled chicken breast (white meat). No skin
  allowed.
Brown rice
One green vegetable or light salad (no dressing
  or oil — only lemon juice)
Coffee, tea, or water (no sugar)

SNACKS

Raw vegetables

As your diet proceeds, you will find that your
skin loosens up. This is the result of fat being lost
under the skin. Try to judge whether you are losing fat at the correct rate. If you are losing too

fast, eat a little more. If the scales show no reduction, get stricter with your diet. If you are in a situation where you need to eat more, don't opt for junk. A quick doughnut or hot dog is not the right way to keep your calories up.

As suggested earlier, neither I nor anyone else can tell you exactly how many calories you should be ingesting. We are all individuals with our own metabolic idiosyncrasies. However, to avoid your body "shutting down" its metabolic rate (and hoarding calories), don't allow your calorie consumption to go below 1500 for men or 1200 for women.

If things are still not coming together as you had hoped, increase aerobic activity rather than further decreasing calorie consumption. Only as a last resort, when during the last fortnight prior to your show, if you are considerably overweight, should you decrease your calories below the suggested minimum levels.

Which is the best aerobic activity for bodybuilders? Probably stationary bike riding, since only the legs move. Aerobic activities like swimming, skiing, racquetball, and tennis are not good for bodybuilders. Too much size is lost when the arms are involved in excessive motion.

Your most critical period of ripping up is the last seven to ten days before the competition. As you approach the seven-day countdown to D-day, cut out all salt (sodium) from the diet. (Prior to this allow normal salt intake.) This includes every food or drink that might contain sodium. You'll have to check all labels for sodium content. Avoid airline foods or restaurant foods, both of which are high in sodium. If you are traveling, prepare your own food beforehand. Make sure it's sodium free because sodium holds water under the skin, up to 180 times its own weight. You may be surprised to learn that sodium is found in many seemingly innocent foods such as:

Artichokes	Celery
Beets	Celery root
Broccoli	Chard (very high)
Brussels sprouts	Collards
Cabbage	Kale
Carrots	Lettuce
Cauliflower	Mushrooms

Parsley	Beef
Peas	Chicken
Spinach	Duck
Tomato	Lamb
Turnip	Pork
Watercress	Turkey
Cantaloupe	
Honeydew melon	Bass
	Canned salmon
Bagels	(very high)
Brown rice	Clams
Cooked oats	Cod
Cornbread (very high)	Flatfish
Corn grits	Haddock
Sunflower seeds	Halibut
Wheat germ	Mullet
Whole wheat bread	Ocean perch
	Oysters
Cheddar cheese	Pike
Cottage cheese (very high)	Pink salmon
Milk	Scallops
Ricotta	Shrimp
Yogurt	Tuna
	Whitefish

Other foods that contain only traces of sodium or none at all are:

Fresh yellow corn	Equal/NutraSweet artificial sweetener
Green bulb onion	
Hot green pepper	
Squash	Brook trout
	Lake trout
Dark buckwheat flour	Crab meat
Raw unhulled pumpkin seeds	Octopus
Lime juice	Corn oil
Vinegar	Olive oil
	Safflower oil
	Unsalted butter

Occasionally you will be forced to eat at a restaurant. Have a special talk with the chef and explain the situation to him. Tell him or her that you must not have *any* salt in your food. You could even exaggerate a little and say that it's a life-and-death situation. I suggest you pretty well stick to egg whites (poached or boiled), plain

Lee Labrada.

John Grimek, Steve Reeves, George Eiferman, Armand Tanny, and Bob McCune.

baked potatoes, and fresh fruit. A good rule is: If you don't know the sodium content, don't eat it! This should even apply to water. Drink only distilled water during the last week.

Your training during the last week should be halted on the Wednesday or Thursday prior to the Saturday competition. A few people like to train right up to the night before, but most find that making Wednesday's workout the last gym training session is the best method. The remaining days prior to competing should be spent mainly posing and relaxing.

Glycogen (carbohydrate stored in the muscles) holds three grams of water per carbohydrate gram. If you eat too little carbohydrate you will flatten the muscles. Too much will puff (bloat) them up. There is an ingredient that will help you balance the water in the muscle and minimize its

existence just under the skin. That substance is potassium. During the last three to six days prior to a contest, your low-sodium diet should be co-ordinated with potassium supplementation. Again, the exact dosage can vary, but the practicing experts generally agree that a 200-pound bodybuilder should take about 100 milligrams five times daily (total 500 milligrams). Take potassium supplements at mealtimes, not on an empty stomach.

Sodium loading is a trick that some, not all, bodybuilders use when preparing for a show. Writer Bill Dobbins is the man behind the promotion of this method, having written several articles about it in the popular muscle-press. Because the body is a homeostatic organism (always having to keep things in balance), when you ingest high levels of sodium it will tend to

Gary Strydom and Michael Ashley.

conserve potassium to keep the two in balance. Therefore, if you ingest fairly high levels of sodium it will tend to conserve potassium to keep the two in balance. Subsequently, if you take in fairly high levels of sodium (but not megadoses) for a week or so prior to going on a low-sodium diet program, when you ultimately do reduce your sodium intake during the last few days before competing you will have naturally high levels of potassium, resulting in a pronounced potassium/sodium imbalance. This will lead to a movement of water *into* the cells, where it is needed to increase mass, and *out* from under the skin, where it serves to "kill" definition. Keep to your low-sodium intake during the last three days and increase potassium supplementation. This further aids the imbalance.

Another trick that pro bodybuilders use just before a contest is to cut daily carbohydrate intake to as little as thirty to fifty grams, seven to ten days prior to show time . . . for two days or so, and then as the competition approaches, they load up, or "carb up," by taking complex carbohydrates during the last three or four days to build (glycogen) levels so that their muscles are full and rotund when they are on stage in front of the judges. These carbs should be taken every two or three hours (except during sleeping time at night) in small quantities. Best foods for the job are potatoes and yams. Do not carb up with simple carbohydrates such as ice cream, sugar, or sherbet.

When you have emptied your muscles of glycogen at the end of your carbohydrate-depletion period, you will find that when you eat carbs you will become bigger, harder, and more vascular and even more defined. It's like a miracle.

Water is pulled from under your skin into the muscle cells. Your muscles suck up carbs like a vacuum, and, because of earlier deprivation, they will store four to five grams of glycogen per 100 grams of muscle weight instead of the usual two to three grams per 100 grams of muscle weight.

How much carbing up should you do? The body can accept only a certain amount at any one time, so big meals are out. Eat small amounts regularly (every two to three hours). Expert Bill Dobbins says: "A minimum of twenty-five grams of carbohydrate per hour, per day." (An average baked potato.)

During the last three to four carbing-up days, you should drink moderate amounts of *distilled* water. You will also have a need for some protein and very small amounts of fat. You can eat some lean beef at this stage.

Do remember that carbing-up success is dependent on whether you can lose all your fat and be five pounds less than your contest weight a week before the show. If you still have to lose weight right up to the time of the competition, you should have begun dieting earlier.

Ripping up for a contest can be tough. Even so, if you are serious about your bodybuilding, you should practice carbohydrate depletion and loading a few times before your contest so you know how you respond to the process. Trial runs will fine-tune the process.